Introduction to
ANTENNAS

by
Louis M. Dezettel

radio shack
A TANDY CORPORATION COMPANY

FIRST EDITION

FIFTH PRINTING—1975

Library of Congress Catalog Card Number: 72-76079

PREFACE

A comprehensive easy to understand guide to antennas has long been needed. In this book the selection, operation, and installation of CB (Citizens band) antennas, as well as fm and tv antennas, are covered in detail.

The choice of a tv antenna could be left to chance. Rushing down and buying that bargain tv antenna you saw advertised may seem like the smart thing to do, and the results may well be satisfactory. The instructions which come with the antenna are frequently adequate for its installation. However, it would be wrong to assume that *any* antenna can assure good results. The chances of success are even less if you are operating a color set.

The problem is not usually in the installation of a tv antenna, but in its selection. Purchasing the right antenna requires considering a number of factors—how far the tv stations are from you; whether or not there are obstructions or nearby conductive masses to product ghosts; how many tv sets are to be operated from the one antenna; whether there are just vhf stations, just uhf stations, or both types in your area; and other factors.

The minutes spent reading this book will give you the ability to evaluate these points and make an intelligent choice of an antenna that will assure good results in your home. You probably have made a large investment already in a color tv set. Protect that investment and enjoy good color reception by the right choice of antenna and a good installation.

While the installation of an antenna usually offers no problems, certain precautions must be observed: how to prevent color fringing, how to be sure your antenna will stay up in a high wind, and how to protect against lightning. All these precautionary methods and more are covered in this book.

To install an antenna properly and to obtain the best possible results, does *not* take a knowledge of electronics, as a reading of this book will show. This book is written in simple terms so the average homeowner can make a correct selection and a good installation.

A federal license to operate Citizens band equipment is available to every citizen of the United States, for a small fee on application. You do not have to have a technical mind to enjoy the advantages of two-way radiocommunication, and you don't have to hire a technical service to install a home or mobile antenna for hookup to your Citizens band equipment. The last few chapters of this book are devoted to antennas for the Citizens band operator—what they are and how to install them.

Louis M. Dezettel

CONTENTS

CHAPTER 1

RADIO WAVES

What is this mysterious power which is sent out by a tv station and picked up and made into something intelligent by thousands of receivers? What is that which takes place in our atmosphere to which the human body does not respond or cannot detect?

This mysterious power, which we call radio waves, is actually electromagnetic energy. The word radio is used to indicate it is used for radiocommunication. The word "waves" means that it radiates outward in a wavelike fashion, as shown in Fig. 1-1. Since it is electromagnetic, it is related to the common permanent magnet with which we are all acquainted. With all of our vast, accumulated knowledge, very little is known about magnetism. We can't feel it, see it, or hear it, although we can observe and measure the effects.

At some time during your life you learned that a horseshoe magnet has a north and a south pole, each at opposite ends of the magnet. A magnetic field is developed around each pole independently. Near the magnet, place a loop of wire terminating in a sensitive current-measuring device (galvanometer). Rotate the magnet, and the changing magnetic field will produce a current in the wire, first in one direction, then the other (Fig. 1-2). At moderate speeds of rotation (3600 revolutions per minute), it would produce 60 complete changes each second, equivalent to the 60-Hz house current in our homes.

Basic ac generators have revolving coils within the magnet structure. Fig. 1-3 is a simplified version of it.

Disconnect the galvanometer in Fig. 1-2. Connect a ground wire to one end of the lead and an antenna to the other. Now

Fig. 1-1. Transmitting wavelike radio power.

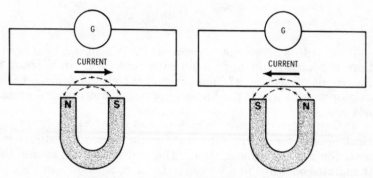

Fig. 1-2. Creating alternating current by rotating a magnet.

move the magnet fast enough, and the antenna will radiate electromagnetic waves which can travel for thousands of miles.

While the above is an oversimplification, it does illustrate what an electromagnetic wave is. The changes in magnetic polarity are called frequency in radio language. A one million

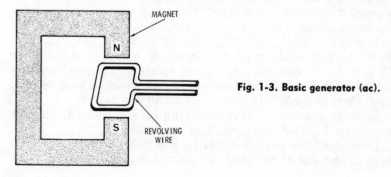

MAGNET

N

Fig. 1-3. Basic generator (ac).

REVOLVING WIRE

S

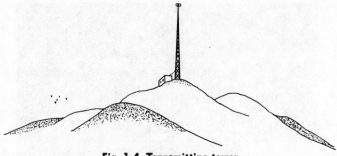

Fig. 1-4. Transmitting tower.

times per second change is called one million cycles per second, and even more correctly 1 MHz.

Of course a radio or tv station doesn't spin a magnet or a coil to develop their radio signal. They use high-powered tubes and involved circuitry to produce an alternating current in the antenna. The alternating current in the conductors of the antenna produces an alternating electromagnetic force that radiates out to your radio or tv set (Fig. 1-4).

RADIO WAVES AND LIGHT WAVES

There are similarities between radio waves and light waves. Although both vary in polarity at a high rate of frequency, light waves involve photons that radiate outward in wavelike fashion. Light waves will pass through glass but are stopped by opaque materials. Radio waves will pass through non-metallic substances but are stopped by metal objects or other materials that are electrically conductive. Light may be reflected by a mirror or polished metal. Radio waves are also reflected by conductive materials, and this fact sometimes gives us trouble, especially in the reception of tv signals. Light, as well as radio waves, may be concentrated in one direction by a parabolic reflector. At very high frequencies, called microwave frequencies, antennas are designed somewhat like searchlight reflectors. You have seen them on top of high towers out in the country on high ground, or on top of telephone company buildings (Fig. 1-5). They are also called "dishpan" antennas, and they increase the power of a radio signal in one direction. They are used to relay tv signals across country and to carry telephone messages.

There is another similarity between light waves and radio waves. When you turn the channel knob on your tv set, you are selecting circuitry that receives only the frequency produced by

Fig. 1-5. Parabolic reflectors mounted on towers.

a particular tv station. Television stations, broadcast stations, and other communication stations are assigned a frequency over which they operate. You can pick the one you want to hear. If you could not, you would hear a jumble of all the signals. The different colors of light are also different frequencies. White light is a combination of all visible light. By placing a colored filter in front of the white light, you would radiate only one color. The colored filters could also act like a tunable receiver, since when you hold a colored filter in front of you, only the color of that filter would be seen from a white-light source.

DIRECT AND REFLECTED WAVES

The effect of large masses of conductive material on radio waves can play havoc on tv signals. The best signal occurs when there is a direct and unobstructed path between the station and your tv set. This is called "line-of-sight" operation (Fig. 1-6).

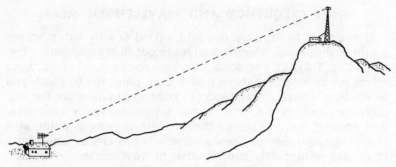

Fig. 1-6. Line-of-sight transmission.

If a large building is in the path, it can reduce the strength of the signal considerably. For this reason, reception inside a large, steel building is often quite poor. The steel in the building acts like a partial shield around your set.

One of the advantages of a reflected signal is in the reception of short-wave stations from great distances. Signals in the 3-MHz to 30-MHz frequency range are reflected or bent by a high ionospheric layer and are reflected back, traveling thousands of miles and making long distance communication possible (Fig. 1-7). If it were not for this, the signals would be lost over the horizon. Television signals are too high in frequency to be reflected by the ionosphere, and go right through it. Therefore, tv signals are line-of-sight only, which is why transmitters put their antennas on high buildings or mountain tops. Also, the higher the receiving antenna, the better the received signal.

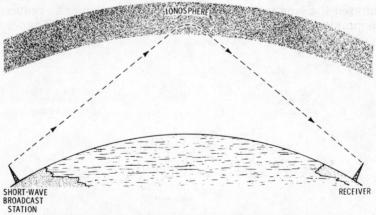

Fig. 1-7. Radio frequencies being reflected by the ionosphere.

WHAT FREQUENCY AND WAVELENGTH MEAN

If you were to drop a stone into a pond of still water, waves would be developed which would move out in ever-widening circles (Fig. 1-8). If you were to measure the number of wave crests per second that move past a fixed point in the pond, you would be measuring frequency. If you were to measure the distance between crests, you would be measuring wavelength. The greater the number of wave crests passing a point at a given time, the shorter the distance between crests. Therefore, frequency is inversely proportional to wavelength.

Radio waves work the same way. They move away from the antenna at a fixed speed, 186,000 miles per second or 300,000,000 meters per second. The polarity changes at a high rate. Broadcast stations (a-m) may transmit a signal frequency anywhere between 535 kHz (535,000 cycles per second) and 1605 kHz (1,605,000 cycles per second) depending on the frequency assigned by the Federal Communications Commission. Many years ago, their frequency was spoken of in terms of wavelength in meters instead of frequency, and some very old sets are still marked in meters. Divide frequency into 300,000,-000 and you get the wavelength in meters. Divide the wavelength in meters into 300,000,000 and you get frequency.

The word meter is still used to describe certain frequency groups or bands. Amateurs will say "75-meter band" for the range of 3.5 to 4.0 MHz, "40-meter band" for the 7.0 to 7.3 MHz range, etc. Those readers interested in the Citizens band around 27 MHz will sometimes hear it expressed as the "11-meter band."

The science of tv is more recent, therefore meters never entered the language. Even reference to frequency is reduced to simple channel numbers. It is simpler to think of Channel 4

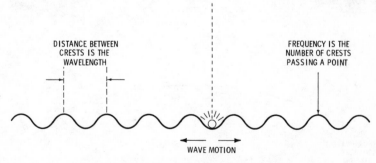

DISTANCE BETWEEN CRESTS IS THE WAVELENGTH

FREQUENCY IS THE NUMBER OF CRESTS PASSING A POINT

WAVE MOTION

Fig. 1-8. Example of wavelength and frequency.

Table 1-1. VHF Channels, Carriers, and Subcarriers*

Channel	Frequency Limits	Picture Carrier	Color Subcarrier	Sound Subcarrier
2	54-60	55.25	58.83	59.75
3	60-66	61.25	64.83	65.75
4	66-72	67.25	70.83	71.75
5	76-82	77.25	80.83	81.75
6	82-88	83.25	86.83	87.75
FM	88-108	—	—	—
7	174-180	175.25	178.83	179.75
8	180-186	181.25	184.83	185.75
9	186-192	187.25	190.83	191.75
10	192-198	193.25	196.83	197.75
11	198-204	199.25	202.83	203.75
12	204-210	205.25	208.83	209.75
13	210-216	211.25	214.83	215.75

* All frequencies in megahertz.

rather than a 67.25 MHz frequency. Table 1-1 lists the tv channels and the actual frequencies of the picture signals. Each tv channel also carries a subcarrier for sound. It is set at just 4.5 MHz higher than the picture carrier frequency. In addition, a color subcarrier is 3.58 MHz higher than the picture-carrier frequency. Uhf tv channels from 14 to 83 are in the frequency range from 470 MHz to 890 MHz.

Broadcast and fm band radio dials have also been simplified. Most broadcast band receiver dials are marked from 55 to 150. The last digit of the actual frequency in megahertz is dropped off. This is also true of the fm band receiver dials.

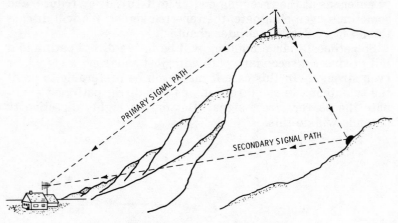

Fig. 1-9. Secondary path can produce ghosts.

13

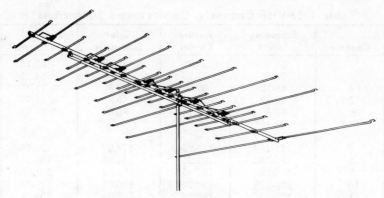

Fig. 1-10. Highly directive antenna.

MULTIPATH SIGNALS

There may be a direct path between you and the tv station, but if there is a large mass off to one side (Fig. 1-9) you may get two signals, one direct and one bounced off the large mass. Although radio waves travel 186,000 miles per second, there is a slight delay in time between the two signals because of the longer path of the second one, so one signal arrives slightly behind the other. This gives rise to ghosts in your picture—another image slightly to the right of the main image. The large mass may be another high building, a mountain, a water tower, or any other large object that is electrically conductive. This is the reason for the importance of using highly directive tv antennas at the receiving end (Fig. 1-10). They reduce, and sometimes even eliminate, the reflected signal. We will discuss this in more detail in a later chapter.

Sometimes a large building will be in the direct path and a hill produces a secondary path with just as strong a signal, or even stronger. In this case it may even be preferable to point the tv antenna in the direction of the indirect path and eliminate the poorer direct signal. But only a highly directive tv antenna will do this.

CHAPTER 2

WHAT ANTENNAS DO

Thousands of watts of radio-wave power, transmitted from a tv or other transmitting antenna, are radiated outward. By the time they get to your receiving antenna very little is left. For the mathematically minded, the loss of power is the same as for light—the inverse-square law applies. That is, the loss is in *inverse* proportion to the *square* of the distance (Fig. 2-1). The light passing through a 1-sq ft window at a distance of one foot would cover a 4-sq ft area at two feet. The intensity of the light at a single point at a distance of two feet is one-fourth that at one foot. This is the inverse-square law, and it applies as well to the decrease in power of a radio wave as it travels away from a transmitter. The amount of power your tv antenna actually feeds to your set may be on the order of two or three hundred microwatts (millionths of a watt). It is for this reason that it is important to use a highly efficient antenna, especially if there is any appreciable distance between the transmitter and the receiver.

RESONANT ANTENNAS

You have probably smiled at the feat of a singer breaking a glass when he hits a certain note. The dimensions of fine glass can be such that when the glass is subjected to vibrations of a certain frequency they will cause stresses in the glass, and it will shatter. Piano strings are different in length, and when struck by the hammer will vibrate at specific musical frequencies. The longer strings (or wires) vibrate at low frequencies and the shorter ones at higher frequencies. These are examples of "resonance." The structure and size of the glass

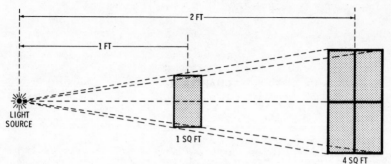

Fig. 2-1. The inverse-square law.

and the length and tautness of the piano strings determine their resonant frequency, or frequency of natural vibration. This is mechanical resonance.

When a length of wire is cut to a specific size, it becomes electrically resonant to radio waves of a specific frequency (Fig. 2-2). When an antenna is resonant, it will do a much better job of converting the feeble radio waves to power that can be used by the receiver. The transmitting antenna is always built to resonate at the transmitting frequency; so are receiving antennas for communication purposes, such as CB antennas. The longer the main element of the antenna, the lower the resonant frequency, as in the case of the piano strings.

In the early days of tv when there were fewer choices of channels on the air, tv receiving antennas were actually made resonant, and some masts and towers had two or three an-

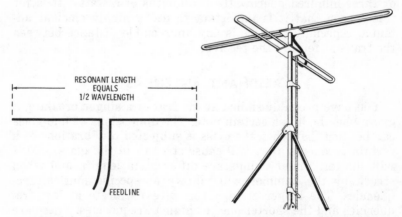

Fig. 2-2. Half-wave dipole.   **Fig. 2-3. Polydirectional fm antenna.**

tennas on them, each dimensioned for a specific tv channel. Television sets were not nearly as sensitive in those days, and every bit of power from the antenna had to be conserved. A current example of a resonant antenna is the Archer fm antenna in Fig. 2-3. It uses two resonant dipoles on one mast, perpendicular to each other, for polydirectional characteristics.

Transmitters and receivers contain resonant circuits within them. When you switch channels in a tv set, you are switching to different resonant circuits. This not only makes the set selective to only the one channel, but increases the sensitivity to that channel. The resonant circuits are in the form of small coils and capacitors, and are called "lumped" resonant circuits, instead of a piece of stretched out aluminum tubing.

But how does a single antenna respond to a number of tv channels, covering the frequency range from 54 MHz to 890 MHz?

BROADBAND ANTENNAS

To overcome the need for multiple antennas for tv reception, a single antenna with multiple elements is used to cover all the channels. While this represents a compromise over the use of a single resonant antenna, modern engineering has developed today's tv antenna to a remarkable degree of efficiency.

Look at a modern tv antenna (Fig. 2-4) and notice the two rows of elements. The two rows are for each half of the vhf Channels, 2 to 6, and 7 to 13. The frequency assignments are not continuous; there is a gap between Channels 6 and 7. In each row the elements are graduated in length, the shortest elements being approximately resonant to the highest frequency or highest channel, and the longest to the lowest channel. The

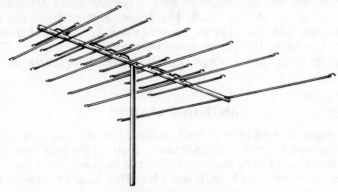

Fig. 2-4. Modern tv antenna.

design is such as to give overlapping frequency coverage to all channels.

There is further value to this type of construction. Each longer element acts like a reflector to the element in front of it. In this way, some of radio wave energy getting past an element is reflected back to the shorter element in front, for increased signal strength. So, not only is a modern tv antenna broadband in its ability to pick up all channels, but it has directional qualities. Its pickup is greater from in front than from the rear or sides. This directional effect is very important in the reduction of images, as mentioned in Chapter 1.

There is a limit to the broadband reception capabilities of a tv antenna. There are two frequency ranges, Channels 2 to 13, covering from 54 MHz to 216 MHz, and Channels 14 to 83, covering from 470 MHz to 890 MHz. The latter range is called uhf, and is widely separated from the vhf range of Channels 2 to 13. Look closely at a modern vhf/uhf tv antenna (Fig. 2-5)

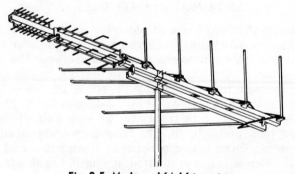

Fig. 2-5. Modern uhf/vhf tv antenna.

and you will see a number of longer elements and a separate group of much shorter ones. The longer elements are for the vhf range, and the shorter elements are for the uhf range. What we have, therefore, are two tv antennas in one. The design is such that a single lead-in serves both parts of the antenna.

ANTENNA LEAD-IN

The quality and type of lead-in from the antenna to a tv set is important in critical installations. That is, for best reception of color where the tv station is at some distance from your location, or where the lead-in must be extra long because of the position of the antenna, lead-in quality becomes important.

There are basically two types of lead-ins (Fig. 2-6). The most popular consists of two parallel wires separated by an insulation material. This is called twin lead, or 300-ohm twin lead. It consists of two wires; each wire has several small-sized wires twisted together to form one larger size. The insulation which holds the wires parallel is flexible polyethylene. The other type of lead-in is coaxial cable. It has a single central wire, either solid or stranded, surrounded by a polyethylene insulation, which in turn is surrounded by a braided outer-wire shield. This shield is in turn covered with a polyethylene outer jacket. Coaxial cables come in various sizes and types and are designated by a code beginning with the letters RG, followed by a number. The one used mostly for tv antennas is RG-59/U.

One advantage of coaxial cable is its shielding effect due to the outer braid. Being round, also, the cable is more easily run from one point to another. However, its principal feature is in the shielding. It is not too important that the cable be kept from sources of possible noises such as lines feeding a universal or brush-type motor, or belt-driven motors in which static noises can be developed by the belt, or near ac lines connected to thermostatic switches.

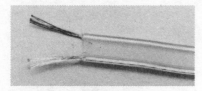   

(A) Twin lead.   (B) Coaxial cable.

Fig. 2-6. Antenna cable.

The quality of tv lead-in wires has to do with the quality of the polyethylene insulation. The better quality is thicker and of purer material. The clearer the color (a milky white) the better the quality. Polyethylene has a tendency to deteriorate with time. It is important to purchase good new stock, and to replace the cable every few years, as determined by a changing picture quality. Superior twin lead has a foam polyethylene insulation. Its weblike structure contains tiny air pockets which improve on the insulation qualities and a dense, outer jacket to reduce the penetration of ultraviolet rays. This Radio Shack cable carries a life guarantee of 20 years.

A shielded 300-ohm twin lead is also available. This provides the shielding against pickup of electrical noises and isolation from effects of nearby metal objects, without changing to the 75-ohm coaxial cable.

IMPEDANCE MATCHING

Don't let this term stop you, as we will not dwell on it long. If you are a hi-fi bug you know that speakers have an impedance of 8 ohms, or 16 ohms. But the output stage of the amplifier, whether transistorized or vacuum tubes, produces its greatest undistorted output power when it drives a certain impedance, usually much higher in value than 8 or 16 ohms. A transformer in the amplifier changes one impedance to the other. The point is the amplifier must "see" the proper im-

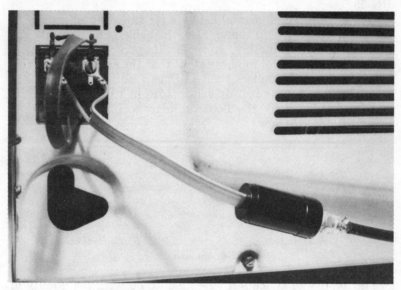

Fig. 2-7. Impedance-matching transformer.

pedance for maximum power. The amplifier is the "source" and the speaker or speakers are the "load." The same is true in a tv set. The lead-in is the "source" and the tv set is the "load."

Most tv sets are designed to have a 300-ohm input impedance. Therefore, the 300-ohm twin lead mentioned earlier does match the set. Some color tv sets are designed for 75 ohms input, and coaxial cable is the correct match. Most modern day color tv sets have a 300-ohm input, so a transformer is used to change the 75-ohm impedance of coaxial cable to 300 ohms, if coaxial cable is used (Fig. 2-7).

Another point where impedance matching is important is between the antenna and lead-in. Most tv antennas are designed to match the usual 300-ohm twin lead. A few antennas are designed for matching directly to 75-ohm coaxial cable. Where they are not matched, a transformer at the antenna can provide that match.

There is another reason why it is important to match impedances for tv. Lead-ins are of a certain length, and they are also resonant to a certain frequency, depending on that length. A resonant lead-in can set up ghosts on the picture. In the case of color, color fringes can develop from a resonant lead-in. However, when the impedance is matched, the lead-in is non-resonant.

Impedance matching, therefore, is important to save every bit of that feeble tv signal and get it to the tv set, and to reduce the possibility of producing additional ghosts from the lead-in.

DIFFERENCE BETWEEN TV, FM, AND CB ANTENNAS

The difference between these basic types is one essentially of decreasing frequency coverage from a single antenna. Here it is in a nutshell.

TV Antenna. Two groups of increasing size elements for covering the range from 54 MHz to 216 MHz, and from 470 MHz to 890 MHz. Each larger element size acts like a reflector to the one in front of it, giving the antenna a unidirectional reception pattern.

FM Antenna. The simplest type is a single element, folded over and called a folded dipole. This single dipole is capable of covering the limited frequency range from 88 MHz to 108 MHz. Because fm stations may be in different directions from your location, a common type is a dual dipole to give polydirectional pattern reception (Fig. 2-3).

CB Antenna. A quite sharply resonant antenna, as it needs only to cover a range from 26.965 MHz to 27.255 MHz of the 11-meter CB band. Most CB antennas are a single element in a vertical position, called a quarter-wave vertical. Some CB buffs who want to increase the effective radiated power will resort to a beam-type antenna very much like radio amateurs do. These are mounted on a rotator for changing direction. The quarter-wave vertical is easy to mount onto a car for mobile operation. The last three chapters of this book cover the subject of CB antennas.

CHAPTER 3

TV ANTENNAS

As indicated in Chapter 2, tv antennas must be designed to receive a very wide band of frequencies for the many tv channels, and receive them with highest possible efficiency. The antenna engineers must be honored for developing today's design which makes possible such wide-band coverage, along with high unidirectional characteristics and high sensitivity. To see the engineering behind an antenna, let us look briefly once again at the tv channel frequencies.

VHF AND UHF TV CHANNELS

Fig. 3-1 is a chart of the radio frequencies between the be-beginning of the broadcast band and the tv frequencies. The scale is logarithmic or the chart would run way off the page.

The spaces between the broadcast band and the beginning of the tv channels are occupied by commercial stations, foreign broadcasts, amateur activities, government and military frequency assignments, etc. Note the gap between Channels 6 and 7. The section between Channels 2 and 6 is called the low-vhf band, and the section between Channels 7 and 13 is the high-vhf band. Although we talk about Channels 2 through 13 being the vhf tv band, as though it were a continuous band, you can see that it is not.

The frequency of each channel in the high-vhf band happens to be about three times the frequency of those in the low-vhf band. (See the table in Chapter 1.) This is fortunate to some tv antenna design. The lengths of the elements used in the low-vhf band, each about one-half wavelength in length, become three half-wave dipoles to the high-vhf band. Therefore,

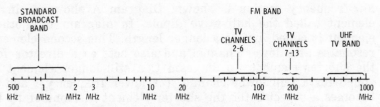

Fig. 3-1. Logarithmically scaled chart of the frequency spectrum.

the same elements can, with performance compromise, serve both sections of the vhf band.

Archer antennas do not compromise the performance of the higher-vhf band but, instead, add the shorter elements as dipoles for this section. This is easily seen in Fig. 3-2. While the

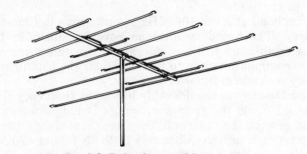

Fig. 3-2. Eight-element vhf tv antenna.

shorter elements appear to be about one-third the length of the longer elements, they are truly half-wave dipoles in the channels from 7 to 13.

The four diagrams in Fig. 3-3 carry us through the evolution of a four-element vhf antenna. For the sake of clarity only the

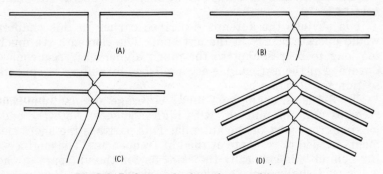

Fig. 3-3. Evolution of a four-element vhf antenna.

23

low-frequency section is shown. Diagram A shows a single element called the half-wave dipole. In diagram B another element is added, but at a longer length. This second element resonates at a lower channel and also acts as a director for the shorter element. In diagram C a still longer element is added for a still lower channel (or lower frequency), and it becomes a reflector for the shorter element in front of it. In diagram D a fourth and still longer element is added. It becomes a reflector to the shorter element, as well as resonating near the low-frequency end of the low-section vhf band, or near Channel 2. To aid in the directivity of this antenna, the elements are bent forward.

The above illustration shows each element connected to the lead-in, in a system called cross-phasing. In some antenna designs, director and reflector elements are added but not connected to the lead-in.

The fm band at 88 to 108 MHz is just above tv Channel 6 in frequency. The broad tv antenna coverage includes the fm band. A tv antenna will also operate an fm tuner or receiver, and it is common practice to take a tap off the lead-in to serve both a tv set and fm tuner or receiver.

The uhf bands are considerably higher in frequency than the vhf bands. While the frequency range is not broken up into sections as with the vhf band, they are divided into two parts for two types of service. Channels 14 to 70 (about 470 MHz to 812 MHz) are for regular tv broadcasts. Channels 71 to 83 (about 812 MHz to 890 MHz) are for translator service. Translators are located in smaller communities and act as relays for programs originating in a nearby metropolitan city. They are automatic in operation; that is, they are unmanned. Thus, communities too far from regular tv stations have tv service.

Very large cities with more tv stations than can fit in the vhf bands will also have uhf tv stations. These operate in Channels 14 to 70.

It is obvious the antenna described earlier in this chapter would operate poorly in the uhf band. The elements are much too long to be resonant to the much higher uhf frequencies. Coverage of the uhf band is accomplished by adding a separate section to the same boom.

Fig. 3-4 is an example of an all-coverage antenna, one that receives vhf, fm, and uhf with high efficiency. Note the odd-looking front part of the antenna. This part has the short elements needed to resonate at the uhf frequencies. The engineering behind it is generally the same as for the vhf part of the antenna. Usually more elements are used, because the overall

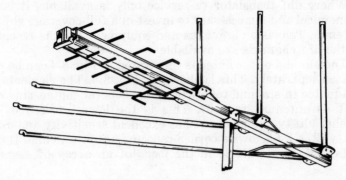

Fig. 3-4. All-coverage antenna.

frequency coverage is greater and more sensitivity is needed to overcome the greater losses encountered at such high frequencies.

Losses are somewhat greater at uhf frequencies than at vhf frequencies, both in the transmission and the reception. Hills, trees, terrain, and other obstructions affect the transmission more at uhf than at vhf frequencies. Television set sensitivity is less at uhf. Losses are greater in the lead-in. This is why distance specifications on tv antennas are less for uhf than for vhf.

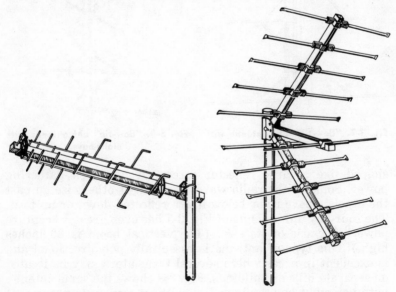

Fig. 3-5. Uhf antenna.   Fig. 3-6. Corner-reflector
                                                 uhf antenna.

Where uhf translator tv service only is available, it is un-
economical and unnecessary to invest in a full-coverage vhf-uhf
antenna. Television antennas and equipment for the reception
of the uhf channels are available.

The uhf end of the antenna illustrated in Fig. 3-4 can be purchased separately. This is shown in Fig. 3-5. The elements are
graduated in size and follow the same general engineering con-
cept as antennas for vhf. This is the lowest priced of the
Archer uhf tv antennas and has excellent sensitivity and directivity. Fig. 3-6 shows a corner-reflector uhf tv antenna. It consists of a single dipole in the locus of an array of elements

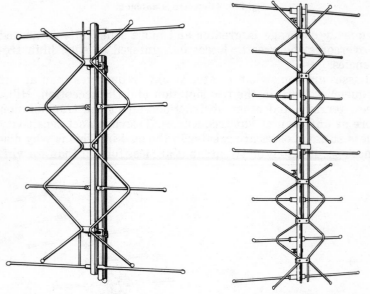

Fig. 3-7. "Bow-tie" uhf antenna with   Fig. 3-8. "Bow-tie" uhf antenna with
           four bays.   eight bays.

shaped like a large reflector screen. It has high gathering
power. Some of the radio waves that might otherwise go past
the dipole, above it, or below it are reflected down or up to it.
The four-bay uhf antenna of Fig. 3-7 has even greater "capture
power" because of its size. (The vertical boom is 30 inches
high.) This type of antenna is essentially polydirectional and
is excellent in areas where several translators may be located
on separate hills or buildings. Fig. 3-8 shows the same antenna
but in an eight-bay configuration with an obvious improvement
in gain.

COLOR TV ANTENNAS

In addition to a very wide bandwidth, each individual tv channel covers a rather wide frequency range, as compared to voice communication transmitters, for example. A minimum bandwidth of 4.5 MHz is covered by one tv station. The selectivity of a black and white set just covers that minimum of 4.5 MHz, dropping in sensitivity rather rapidly at the two extremes. A color tv set, however, must have a wider bandwidth, and 6 MHz is about their standard. This is to assure good reception of the added color information on the signal. For those who understand it, the response curve difference between a black and white set and color set is shown in Fig. 3-9. The explanation of it is too technical to go into in this book. The point is, the color information transmitted is in addition to the black and white information, and unless the set can pick up the color information, true colors on the picture tube will not be realized.

Antenna response to color tv signals must be flatter across each channel, in addition to covering the entire bandwidth. That is, the antenna must respond equally to all frequencies on each channel. This makes engineering requirements much tougher, but with the greatly increased use of color sets, nearly all well-engineered antennas are designed for good color reception. This is true of the entire Archer line of outdoor tv antennas. Fig. 3-10 illustrates the top of the Archer line, recommended for deep fringe reception or where high directivity is important. At the other end, even the one shown in Fig. 3-4, selling for less than $16.00, is designed for color tv reception on all tv bands and fm.

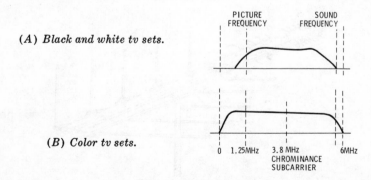

(A) Black and white tv sets.

(B) Color tv sets.

Fig. 3-9. Frequency-response curves.

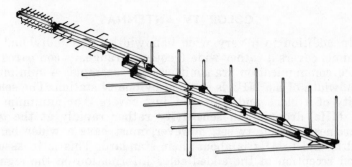

Fig. 3-10. Deep fringe tv antenna.

A stronger signal must be fed into the tv set input for color than for black and white. A weak signal on a black and white set will result in some "snow." If you live some distance from a tv station, you may be tolerating the snow. If now you are contemplating the purchase of a color tv set, you *must* consider improving the antenna system. If you attempt to operate the color set from the same antenna, you will surely suffer in color quality. The 3.58 MHz subcarrier also transmitted with the picture carrier and sound carrier on each channel carries the modulation for color information. Without a strong 3.58 MHz signal, the color information will be lacking and color will be degraded.

An earlier chapter described how ghosts were developed on a picture tube. As with snow, a faint ghost on a black and white set is often tolerated. In a color set it cannot be, as too often the ghosts are of differing color and most annoying. Thus, the antenna must have high unidirectional qualities, to eliminate the secondary transmission path and correct impedance matching to keep the lead-in a nonresonant line. Fig. 3-11 illustrates

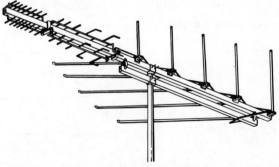

Fig. 3-11. Moderate distance, all-coverage tv antenna.

a good choice of a tv antenna for moderate distances at reasonable cost, yet with a sharp front lobe in its pickup pattern.

ANTENNA ELEMENTS VERSUS DISTANCE

Most catalogs describing tv antennas show the distance over which they will receive good pictures on the vhf bands. With an increase in the number of elements used in the antenna, there is an increase in its ability to reach out for good reception.

Another method of indicating the sensitivity of an antenna is the area over which one may expect good performance. This may be shown as *metro, suburban, medium, fringe,* or *deep fringe.* The words are almost self-explanatory. Metro means metropolitan, or within a city. Suburban means the suburban towns around the metropolitan area, etc.

Because of decreased efficiency in the uhf band, the distance indicated for uhf is usually about 25% less. This varies depending on the type of uhf section added to the antenna.

Keep in mind that the number of elements mentioned for an antenna includes the elements of the uhf section on vhf/fm/uhf antennas. A vhf/fm antenna for the vhf bands (always including the fm band) may only list a greater distance for a fewer number of elements.

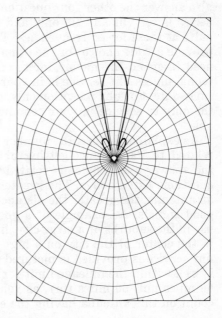

Fig. 3-12. Polar pattern.

The greater distance ability of an antenna is not so much a function of the number of elements directly, but is due to the fact that more elements increase the forward lobe of the polar pattern (Fig. 3-12). With more elements the unidirectional characteristics are improved. By reducing the pickup from the rear and sides, the antenna has better sensitivity to signals from the forward direction.

WHAT ANTENNA TO BUY

Before you buy a tv antenna, you should ask yourself a number of questions.

1. Are the tv stations in your area on the vhf bands only, the uhf band only, or do you have both?
2. How far from the stations' transmitting towers are you?
3. Are the towers in "line-of-sight" or are there buildings, heavy tree growth, hills, or other obstructions in the way?
4. Are you operating a black and white set, or a color tv set?
5. How many tv sets will the same antenna be expected to serve, and is an fm tuner or receiver to be on the line?

If you have both vhf and uhf tv service in your area, then the antenna to purchase is one of the Archer "Color Supreme" series. Among the six models in this line will be one that will also answer the other four questions. The Archer "Color Eagle" series is for vhf and fm only and will provide outstanding results at these lower frequencies. The five models in this series provide a wide choice for the other considerations. There is no need to spend the money for the added uhf section of an antenna, unless uhf service is in your area or is anticipated at an early date. For uhf reception only, or where uhf translators are the only tv service in your community, four models are available.

As explained before, the number of elements in an antenna is related to its distance-getting ability. Here again, however, the answer as to choice is related to the answers to the other questions listed above. The greater the number of elements in an antenna, the greater the distance over which it will bring in good signals. An example of a good choice of an antenna for use in the suburbs of a large city, in which the tv towers are all in the center of the city on a high building, and both vhf and uhf service is provided is pictured in Fig. 3-13. If your suburb is well within the mileage limit for this antenna (90 miles vhf, 60 miles uhf, 60 miles fm), as you almost surely are, you can count on this antenna having the extra directional qualities to eliminate or reduce ghosts, or overcome obstructions, or operate more than one set.

The third question is almost answered in the previous statements. It is hard to determine to what extent there are obstructions in the path of the signal if you cannot see the transmitter tower from the roof of your house. A good check on your antenna need is to talk with a few neighbors. Note the results they get, and the number of elements in the antenna they are using. A building or a stand of trees in the way are not total obstructions. The tv signal does bend around obstructions and to some extent go through them. But when it does, there is a loss of signal strength.

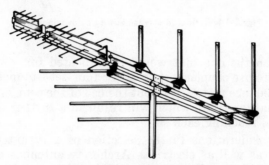

Fig. 3-13. Suburban antenna.

For reasons mentioned earlier in this chapter, the reception of a good signal for color is more important than for black and white. Also, remembering what was said about the need for wide frequency response, it is obvious that the distance from the transmitter is not the paramount consideration in the purchase of a tv antenna for color reception. The investment made in a color set is considerably more than in a black and white set. The investment in an antenna for the set should be in proportion. As a rule of thumb, select an antenna one step up from one that might have been selected for a black and white set. If you live in the metropolitan area, select a suburban antenna. If you live in the suburbs, you should select a medium range antenna, etc.

If you operate more than one set from a single antenna, the low signal power brought to the end of the lead-in will be divided among the number of sets to be connected. Here again, a good rule of thumb is similar to the one mentioned above. If you operate two sets from one antenna, select the next better

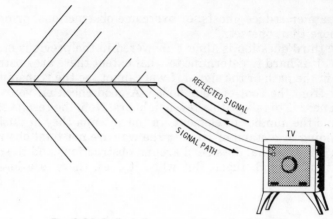

Fig. 3-14. Reflected waves causing color fringing.

antenna than the one that would be indicated for your area. Remember to use couplers—two-set or four-set—to maintain a proper impedance match. Without the use of the couplers, there is no impedance match, which will result in a further decrease in the signal reaching each set.

Other considerations in the selection of a tv antenna are mechanical as well as electrical. Archer tv antennas are supplied preassembled; elements snap into position easily. All are finished in gold vinyl, acrylic, or other weather-resistant material. Installation is easy.

IMPORTANCE OF LEAD-IN

Impedance matching is important, especially for good color. There must be a correct impedance match between the antenna and the lead-in, and between the lead-in and the tv set. If not

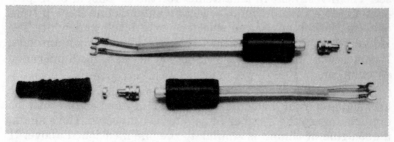

Fig. 3-15. Impedance-matching transformers.

matched, the lead-in will set up reflected waves which will result in color fringing.

The reflected waves result in delayed signals built up in the lead-in. As shown in Fig. 3-14, some of the signal reaching the tv set is reflected back up the lead-in to the antenna, then reflected back down again. The effect is similar to a secondary signal path bounced off a nearby hill or other large object, except that the delay in the lead-in is much shorter. The result is color fringing, rather than an actual visible ghost image on the screen. Under matched conditions there are no reflected waves, therefore no secondary delayed signals and no color fringing.

A good lead-in cable for color is coaxial cable. An installation would include a transformer at the antenna (Fig. 3-15) to change the 300-ohm impedance of the antenna to the 75-ohm impedance of the coaxial cable, and another transformer at the input terminals of the tv set to change the 75-ohm impedance of the coaxial cable back to the 300-ohm impedance of the set. Of course, 300-ohm twin lead could be used for the lead-in, and no transformers would be needed and everything would be matched. But unshielded twin lead, unless very carefully placed, can be troublesome. Lacking a shield it can pick up unwanted noises from nearby sparking or static-producing equipment. Should it come close to other metal, such as a metal gutter at the edge of the house, the capacitive effect of the gutter or other metal object can upset its impedance.

There is a shielded 300-ohm twin-lead cable, made especially for color-tv installations. A Mylar-backed aluminum foil is wrapped over the outside for shielding. The shield is covered by a polyethylene jacket. This cable eliminates the precautions required for carefully placing ordinary twin lead, and also avoids the need of installing transformers at the antenna and the tv set for an impedance change.

ROTATORS AND THEIR IMPORTANCE

As a general rule all tv station antennas are located in one place; either on a tall building in the center of the city, or on top of a high hill or mountain. But this is not always the case. A few places do not combine all tv service in one place. Furthermore, if you live out in the country and are in a position to receive tv service from two or more cities, your tv watching pleasures could be limited if you did not have a method of changing the direction of your antenna.

A central point of transmission is often not the case for fm. Too often, a central high point of transmission for fm entails

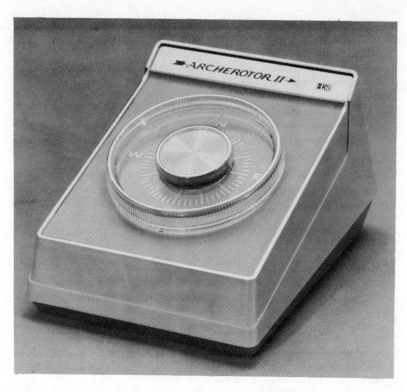

Fig. 3-16. Automatic rotator.

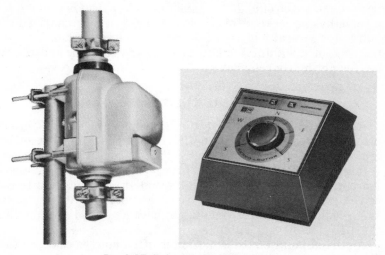

Fig. 3-17. Deluxe automatic rotator.

an expense not compatible with the smaller fm audience compared with tv. If good stereo fm reception is important from the tv antenna, investing in a rotator may be worthwhile. In this way you can swing the antenna around towards the desired fm transmission. This can make the difference between receiving fm with ideal hi-fi conditions, or lower fidelity, especially with stereo.

Television ghosts in the picture result from a second path of transmission from a nearby hill, building, tower, or other ob-

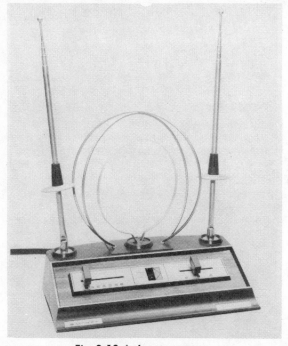

Fig. 3-18. Indoor tv antenna.

ject. The effect may vary from tv channel to channel. One method of overcoming ghosts on tv sets is to mount your tv antenna on a rotator. This allows you to adjust the direction of the antenna for minimum ghost effect. It is sometimes desirable to point the antenna slightly away from the primary tv transmission. While there may be a slight loss in primary signal strength, there could be a much greater loss of the signal from the secondary path, with an overall improvement of picture. Figs. 3-16 and 3-17 show two models of Archer rotators. Setting the dial to the direction starts the motor turning, stopping automatically at the desired point.

INDOOR ANTENNAS

Under some conditions an indoor antenna will give remarkably good results. In a small city, consisting primarily of homes, obstructions in the path of the signal can be at a minimum and an indoor antenna will operate quite well. The better indoor antennas are adjustable as to signal frequency and impedance match (Fig. 3-18). A complete chapter is devoted to this subject later on.

CHAPTER 4

SPECIAL ANTENNAS FOR FM

The fm frequency band range is 88 to 108 MHz. It starts just off the high frequency end of tv Channel 6. That is why a tv antenna also receives fm signals quite well, and the same antenna can be shared between a tv set and an fm tuner or receiver. In addition, a good fm tuner has much higher sensitivity than a tv set and not as much signal is needed from the antenna for good fm reception.

THE RESONANT ANTENNA

Since the fm band is only 20 MHz wide, an fm antenna of simple design can be considered pretty nearly resonant in the fm band. This is why a single element antenna, or single dipole as it is called, does a good job of fm reception. A dipole about 60 inches long is considered resonant in the fm band. At this length it becomes a half-wave dipole, the usual term used in engineering parlance for a resonant antenna. Fig. 4-1 is a drawing of such an antenna. This is called a folded dipole. It is used because the feed point, the point at which a lead-in is connected, has an impedance of 300 ohms and matches the 300-ohm twin lead usually used as the lead-in.

Fig. 4-2 is an illustration of a commercial fm antenna which is probably the most popular of antennas used for fm alone. It is two folded dipoles like the sketch of Fig. 4-1, and is connected to one lead-in.

UNIDIRECTIONAL AND OMNIDIRECTIONAL ANTENNAS

Too often fm transmitting towers are not all located in a single area, as mentioned before. Where this is true, good re-

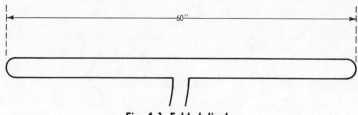

Fig. 4-1. Folded dipole.

ception from all stations requires an antenna that has good pickup from all directions. This type of antenna is called an omnidirectional or polydirectional antenna.

Fig. 4-2. Fm antenna with two folded dipoles.

The antenna illustrated in Fig. 4-1 would have a polar pattern that would look like a figure 8 (Fig. 4-3). It would be good for pickup in the two opposite directions. The antenna of Fig. 4-2 is two folded dipoles at right angles to each other. The polar

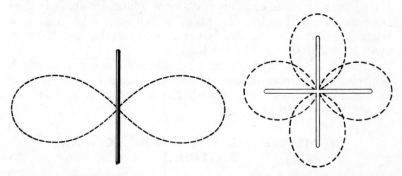

Fig. 4-3. Polar pattern of a single dipole.

Fig. 4-4. Polar pattern of two dipoles set at right angles.

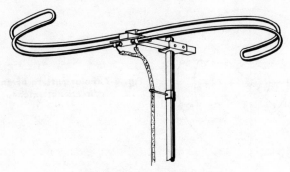

Fig. 4-5. S-curve, fm antenna.

pattern becomes two figure 8's at right angles (Fig. 4-4). Now we have essentially an omnidirectional antenna. In practice the patterns illustrated are never exact, as they are affected by surrounding terrain and other conductive objects and overhead wire systems.

Fig. 4-5 is another omnidirectional antenna. As can be seen, the antenna is a single dipole but bent into an "S" curve. This will distort the normal figure 8 pattern and result in good omnidirectional pickup. The antenna of Fig. 4-2 is to be preferred for best all-around pickup.

If all fm services are in the same direction, or if you are some distance from the stations, the antenna shown in Fig. 4-6 is the best. It uses tv antenna engineering to achieve high unidirectional characteristics, using a reflector and two directors, in addition to the twin-drive elements shown. Its pattern is sharply unidirectional (Fig. 4-7). This gives it the greater pickup sensitivity needed for reception at distances up to 110 miles.

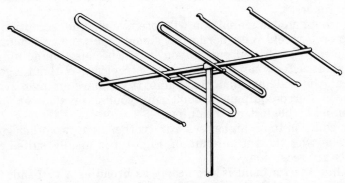

Fig. 4-6. Fm unidirectional antenna.

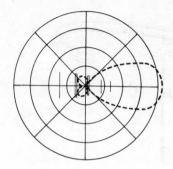

Fig. 4-7. Polar pattern of an fm unidirectional antenna.

STEREO RECEPTION AND ANTENNAS

If you have a good fm tuner or receiver you probably know it has a published sensitivity somewhere between 0.5 μV and 5 μV. This is a considerably higher sensitivity figure than for tv sets. This means that just about any old piece of wire connected to the antenna terminal will give you good enough reception, and often does. However, the better the signal into the tuner or receiver, the better the external and internal noise reduction and the better the reception quality.

This is even more important in receiving two-channel or stereo fm. The fm signal coming into your tuner not only carries the audio information, but includes a 19 kHz signal for use by the multiplex circuit in your tuner. This 19 kHz signal must lock-in with a 19 kHz signal developed in your tuner, or you won't get two-channel audio out. The 19 kHz signal is transmitted at one-tenth the strength of the fm carrier itself. It is for this reason that you must have a good signal input to your tuner, if you want good lock-in with the multiplex circuit in your tuner.

Without a good signal you will lose two-channel reception or the stereo effect. With borderline signal input, the two-channel audio may go in and out as you listen, because changing atmospheric effects can vary the signal strengths. Without a good signal, you will have distorted audio. If you have an investment in good stereo equipment, don't ruin your enjoyment of good listening by neglecting the antenna.

In addition to its higher sensitivity, there are two other good reasons why the fm antenna of Fig. 4-6 is ideally suited for stereo fm reception.

While the fm band is not nearly as broad as a tv band, the 20-MHz bandwidth is equal to about three tv channels in a row.

A single antenna element will not cover the entire fm band with equal sensitivity. The antenna of Fig. 4-6 has two elements connected together, which gives it the name of twin-drive. Each element is a different size, engineered to provide equal signal pickup across the entire fm band. Whether the station is at the low, the middle, or the high end of the fm band, you can be assured of equal reception from any with stereo service.

As in the case of tv, multipath signal reception will affect the fidelity of the signal. When a signal from a secondary path, one reflected from a hill or water tower nearby for example, is received, the longer transmission path results in a slight delay in the signal. Depending on the length of the path, the delay can be partially or fully out-of-phase with the intended signal. An out-of-phase signal tends to act counter to the strength of the original signal and to cancel it to a degree. This reduced strength can affect audio quality in receiving stereo. As in the case of tv reception, a highly unidirectional antenna, such as the one of Fig. 4-6, is the answer.

What do you do if you want the advantages of a unidirectional antenna, but fm stations are all around you? The answer is use a rotator. In this way, you can swing the antenna toward the station you want to pick up and enjoy the best possible signal reception from it.

INDOOR ANTENNAS

Where conditions are right, an indoor antenna can bring quite satisfactory results. Conditions often found in smaller cities, such as fewer tall buildings to get in the way and fm transmitting towers fairly close to you, may not require the high antenna.

Fig. 4-8 is a cabinet-top indoor antenna with adjustable dipole elements, plus a multi-position switch for better impedance matching. The two "rabbit-ear" elements are telescoping, and so may be adjusted in length for best resonance to the fm frequency. A length of 300-ohm twin-lead line is included with the antenna. The rotatable base permits rotating the antenna for best pickup direction.

As in the case of the outdoor single dipole antenna, the pickup pattern is essentially a figure 8. The ideal figure 8 is achieved only when an antenna is assumed to be in *free space*. Free space means it is infinitely high, and there are no metallic obstructions anywhere near it. While this is not ideally achieved even in an outdoor antenna, it is far from achieved with an indoor antenna. Being indoors it is surrounded by conductive

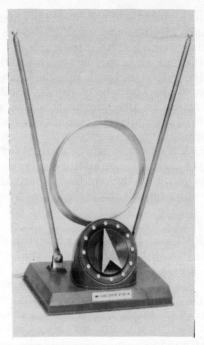

Fig. 4-8. Fm cabinet-top antenna.

objects, such as the electrical wiring in the home, water and sewer pipes, gas pipes, and even the metal corner protectors used in plaster walls. Even the human body is a factor, especially since the height of a person is very nearly a half-wave

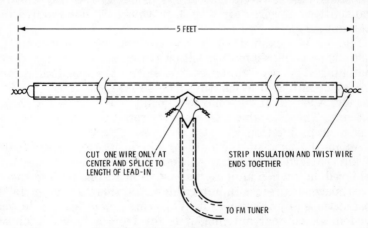

Fig. 4-9. Making an indoor fm antenna.

long at the fm band. (Remember the 60-inch length of a half-wave dipole mentioned for fm earlier.)

What does all this mean? It means there can be obstructions in the path of the signal that will reduce its strength. It means some of the signal can be reflected back to the antenna and either add to or subtract from the signal strength, depending on its distance from the antenna. It means a signal can vary as a person walks around the room. All of this means if you really want good fm reception, especially for stereo, use a good outdoor antenna.

For those who want to make their own indoor fm antenna, the sketch of Fig. 4-9 shows the details. A piece of 300-ohm twin lead is all you need. This antenna can be tacked behind the hi-fi cabinet, but results are better if it can be installed up higher, such as along the picture molding near the ceiling. Its position should be perpendicular to the path or direction of the principal fm station you want to receive.

INSTALLATION

Installation of an outdoor fm antenna is the same as for a tv antenna. A complete chapter on tv antenna installation is given later.

The coaxial cable mentioned for color-tv antenna installation is not needed for fm. However, 300-ohm twin lead can be used, and impedance matching is automatically achieved without transformers. It is important the line be kept clear of other metal objects, such as gutters, by the use of the same standoff insulators used for tv.

CHAPTER 5

FRINGE AREA TV/FM ANTENNAS

The word fringe means the outer area of good tv reception, beyond which enjoyable reception should not be expected. It may be defined as somewhere between 100 and 150 miles, the extremes of which might be named near fringe and deep fringe. The words are rather nebulous and even the distances are not clear, as so much depends on factors and not just distance. Conditions of terrain count as much as distance.

DISTANCE AND SIGNAL STRENGTH

In earlier chapters we discussed the similarity between light and radio waves, and the loss of signal based on the inverse-square law. Signal loss is related to the square of the distance. At 50 miles a signal is only one-fourth as strong as at 25 miles. At 100 miles it is only one-fourth as strong as at 50 miles. At 100 miles it is only *one-sixteenth* as strong as at 25 miles. The sketch of Fig. 5-1 is another method of showing this. To make an even more extreme comparison, city folks living at about 10 miles from a tv transmitter have no problem with tv reception on the basis of distance only. Their "country cousins" living 100 miles from the same transmitter are faced with receiving a signal only one-hundredth as strong, so they must take special steps to make the best of that weak signal.

The inverse-square law is based on free-space conditions; that is, with nothing else interfering. But at the surface of the earth other things do interfere—the horizon and hills or rolling terrain.

Light bends very slightly around the curvature of the earth. The prism effect of the denser atmosphere near the surface and

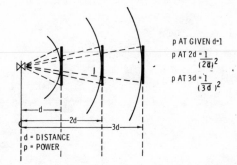

Fig. 5-1. The inverse-square law.

p AT GIVEN d=1

p AT 2d = $\frac{1}{(2d)^2}$

p AT 3d = $\frac{1}{(3d)^2}$

d = DISTANCE
p = POWER

lighter atmosphere higher up is what puts a small bend in light. Radio waves will follow the curvature of the earth much more than light waves, for reasons other than the prism effect of the atmosphere. At low radio frequencies the bend is considerable. This is why you can pick up broadcast stations at night a thousand or more miles away from your car radio as you travel across country. (Long distance transmission is better at night due to rearrangement of the ionized layers.) At higher radio frequencies, radio waves begin to act more and more like light, and the ability to follow the curvature of the earth is less. At tv frequencies the bend is quite small. Hills and other rises in the earth's terrain are even more difficult to overcome. This is why great height is needed, both on the part of the tv transmitter and on the part of the receiving antenna.

A homeowner at a distance from a tv transmitter and in a valley has an almost insurmountable problem in bringing tv entertainment into his home. An individual can install an antenna at the top of a nearby hill, connect an amplifier, and run coaxial cable down to his home. This becomes a rather expensive installation. Communities in a valley will usually contract for a community television installation and service. This is called CATV. A company will install a very high-gain antenna on a hill, amplify the signal from it, and feed the signal to the homes in the community by coaxial cable. A fee is charged to bring the cable into the home, and a monthly service charge helps maintain the equipment.

LONG-RANGE ANTENNAS

To assure good fringe area reception of tv, a high-gain antenna mounted as high as possible is required.

The antenna in Fig. 5-2 is an example of an all-coverage antenna for fringe use. It covers the vhf and uhf tv bands as

45

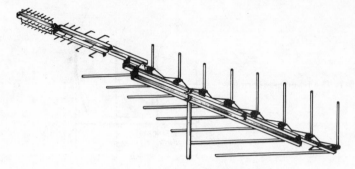

Fig. 5-2. A 35-element fringe antenna.

well as fm. With a total of 35 elements it will receive tv signals on the vhf band up to 150 miles, and on the uhf and tv bands up to 90 miles.

If the tv stations around you broadcast service in Channels 2 to 13 only (the vhf tv band), the antenna in Fig. 5-3 has almost the gain of the one in Fig. 5-2, but at considerably less cost. With its 23 elements it will bring in tv signals from up to 125 miles, and fm up to 100 miles.

In many areas, stations serving the fringe areas may transmit only on the uhf channels, 14 to 70. Also, sometimes the uhf translators on Channels 71 to 83 will be quite a distance from your home. In any case, the uhf antenna in Fig. 5-4 is an eight-bay uhf only tv antenna capable of picking up signals in the uhf channels up to 100 miles away. It is not unidirectional, and is ideal for the reception of stations in different directions from your home.

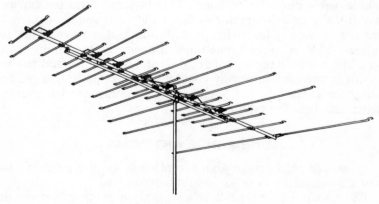

Fig. 5-3. Vhf/fm antenna.

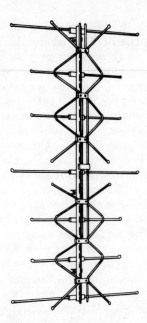

Fig. 5-4. Fringe uhf antenna.

For fringe area fm only, the fm antenna in Fig. 5-5 has high unidirectional characteristics, which give sufficient gain for a 110-mile range.

NEED FOR HEIGHT

The one factor for successful reception of tv in fringe areas, that of high-gain antennas, was described above. The other factor is the need for great height to overcome the effect of the horizon or other hilly obstructions. Height is important for

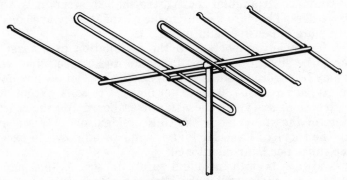

Fig. 5-5. High-gain fm antenna.

both the transmitting and receiving antennas. The tv stations use the highest economical locations they can in order to serve as many viewers as possible. The height of the receiving antenna is up to the owner of the tv set.

One of the best ways of deciding just how much height is needed for your location is to check with neighbors in your area. However, keep a few points in mind when checking with your neighbor. Is he using a black and white set? How much snow, if any, is there in the picture? How does his antenna compare with the one you plan on installing? Is he located on higher ground than your location? If you want good color reception, you will need a better installation than one for black and white.

Height above ground is not the only factor to consider. You must get above any high trees or other obstructions in the path of the signal. An antenna 40 feet above ground is about average for most fringe area installations.

Some areas of the country have the good fortune to be served by transmitting antennas that are quite high. Cities near mountains will usually have tv stations atop a nearby mountain. Los Angeles, Denver, and Albuquerque are among them. Such antenna systems can serve a wide area without necessarily needing high receiving tv antennas. One installed on the roof of the home is often sufficient.

MASTS AND TOWERS

The usual method for installing a tv antenna at great height is atop a mast or tower. Masts, like the one shown in Fig. 5-6, come in 20-, 30-, and 40-foot lengths. They are made in sections with graduated diameters that telescope into each other. The steel masts are hot-dipped galvanized and zinc coated for weather protection.

Towers are triangular or square-shaped structures with cross girders. They are usually made of steel. They are considerably more expensive than masts.

It is extremely important in the installation of a mast or tower to be sure it will withstand the highest possible wind that may be encountered in your area. Highest winds normally encountered are about 80 miles per hour, with some exceptions. The exceptions are along the Atlantic seaboard and the coastal borders of the states along the Gulf of Mexico. In Wisconsin, along the shore of Lake Michigan, winds are known to exceed the 80 miles per hour mentioned.

It is always best to include a safety factor. A 30% safety factor is recommended by the Electronic Industries Associa-

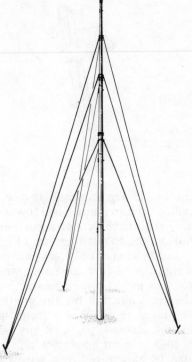

Fig. 5-6. Telescoping steel tower.

tion, which means for highest normal 80 mile-an-hour winds, figure on about 110 miles per hour.

Towers up to fifty feet can usually be installed without guy wires. A two-foot square hole is dug. The mounting feet usually supplied with the mast are put in place, properly spaced to fit the bottom of the tower, and about a yard of concrete is poured into the hole. When the concrete is set, two of the bottom feet of

Fig. 5-7. Erecting a steel tower.

Fig. 5-8. Guy-wire stake.

the tower are fastened to the mounting feet, and the tower pulled up into place. Steel towers are quite heavy, and will probably require the use of a gin pole, a tackle line, and two or three husky men to put them up (Fig. 5-7).

Masts are not only less expensive, but considerably lighter in weight. A 40-foot mast only weighs about 33 pounds. All masts must be guyed, which means there must be enough room around the mast location for the guying stakes. Guying stakes should be placed about 10 feet from the base for each 20 feet of mast height. Radio-type, 6/18 guy wire is sufficiently strong to hold a 40-foot mast in any wind. Size 6/18 means six strands of size 18 galvanized iron wire twisted together. Stakes may be commercial type (Fig. 5-8), or 5- to 10-foot lengths of concrete reinforcement rods, one inch in diameter. They are driven into the earth at an angle, each 120° apart.

Masts are light enough to be mounted on the roof of a house or other structure. It requires careful calculation of the length of the guy wires, which are fastened in place before the mast

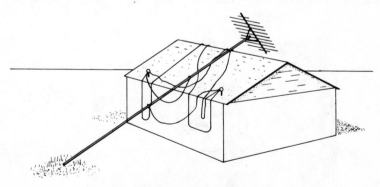

Fig. 5-9. Structure mounted mast.

is raised onto the roof. Fig. 5-9 shows how this is done. The mast can be walked up after the guys are in place. Be sure the guy eye-screws are fastened into roof rafters, or they will surely pull out with a high wind.

The tv antenna, and rotator if used, must be installed on the tower or mast before they are raised. All lead-in and rotator cables must be connected and run down with standoff insulators beforehand. The antenna must be correctly orientated as to direction if a tower is used, as a tower cannot be rotated after it is up. A mast can be rotated after it is in the vertical position, however.

If tv transmitters are located in different directions, or if an offside hill develops a secondary signal path, a rotator is highly recommended. Rotators are geared-down, electric motors that turn the antenna to the direction desired. Some, like the two in the Archer line, have internal brakes to hold the antenna in its correct direction after rotation. Wind whip will not turn the antenna.

An important precaution: Be sure to install your antenna far enough from any electric lines so that it will not fall onto the lines in case it is blown down. Also consider any possible damage to buildings or other structures nearby, either those of your own, or those of your neighbor's. Leave plenty of room around your antenna system.

CHAPTER 6

MULTIPLE-SET DISTRIBUTION

More and more homes now have two or more sets. Two-set homes may nearly equal, if they do not already exceed, the number of homes with one tv set. Also, operating an fm tuner or receiver off the same antenna with a tv set is quite popular.

Assuming a reasonably good antenna and a reasonable distance from the tv station, along with the high sensitivity of the modern tv set, there is no reason why more than one set cannot be operated from a single antenna. In doing so, however, it is advisable to observe certain rules for best results, especially if a color set is one of those on the same line.

IMPEDANCE MATCHING

Only when a lead-in is terminated with a load in its characteristic impedance is the lead-in nonresonant. This may sound a bit complicated, but it only means that a 300-ohm twin line should be connected to a 300-ohm load. When the end of a 300-ohm lead-in is connected directly to the antenna terminals on the back of a single tv set, the set is the 300-ohm load, and the impedance is matched. If two sets are parallel-connected (Fig. 6-1) to the single lead-in, the lead-in "sees" a different impedance. The equivalent impedance will be 150 ohms. This is shown schematically in Fig. 6-2. The point is, two things happen when the lead-in impedance is mismatched: the wires of the lead-in could become resonant at certain frequencies, and produce color fringes in the picture of a color-tv set; signal losses are increased and some of the signal from the antenna is wasted.

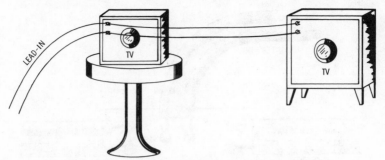

Fig. 6-1. Connecting a single lead-in to two tv sets.

Impedance matching is achieved with the use of transformers. These work like the transformers in the output stage of a hi-fi amplifier, as described in Chapter 2. Special coils change one impedance value to another at minimum loss.

Two types of impedance-matching couplers are generally available. Fig. 6-3 shows a two-set coupler. It has three sets of

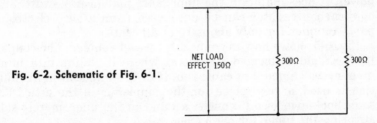

Fig. 6-2. Schematic of Fig. 6-1.

screw terminals. One set is for connecting the lead-in. The other two are for the two sets. The same kind of 300-ohm lead-in wire may be run from the coupler to the tv sets. This is the way it is usually done, with the coupler located somewhere convenient to both sets. Fig. 6-4 shows a four-set coupler. The five sets of terminals are for the lead-in, and for the wires to the four sets. It should be located where distribution cable to each set can be kept to a minimum length.

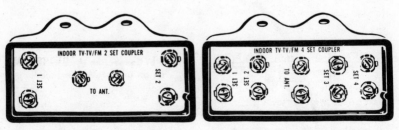

Fig. 6-3. Two-set tv coupler.　　　　Fig. 6-4. Four-set tv coupler.

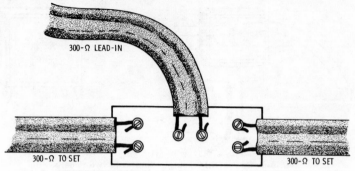

Fig. 6-5. Connecting two tv sets to one antenna.

300-Ω LEAD-IN

300-Ω TO SET

300-Ω TO SET

What do you do when you want to connect to only three tv sets, or two tv sets and an fm tuner? Use a four-set coupler. However, it is best to connect a "dummy load" to the fourth terminal set. All this means is to connect a 300-ohm resistor to the terminals. While this results in a waste of some of the power, it does maintain the impedance match. A ½-watt, 300-ohm carbon resistor can be purchased from a local electronic parts supplier for only about 10 or 12 cents.

Fig. 6-5 shows how to connect a two-set coupler. The coupler itself should be located at a point where it results in a minimum overall amount of cable run. If in-the-wall lead-in installation is used, a good place for the coupler is in the attic. The same hookup is used for one tv set and an fm tuner, merely substituting the tuner for one tv set.

Fig. 6-6 shows the hookup for a four-set coupler. In this diagram three tv sets and an fm tuner are connected to the coupler, and all are operated from a single antenna. Fig. 6-7 shows what a resistor looks like. To substitute the resistor for a tv set, merely bend the two leads of the resistor, twist one lead around each of the screw terminals of the unused set (Fig. 6-8), and tighten the screws.

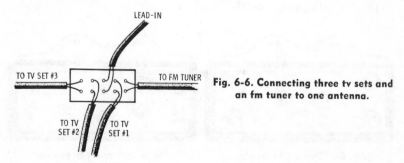

LEAD-IN

TO TV SET #3

TO FM TUNER

TO TV SET #2

TO TV SET #1

Fig. 6-6. Connecting three tv sets and an fm tuner to one antenna.

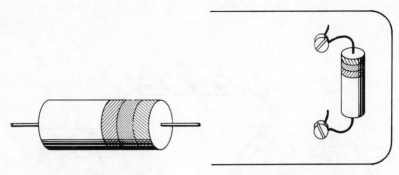

Fig. 6-7. A typical carbon-
composition resistor.

Fig. 6-8. Installing a resistor onto
a coupler.

Sometimes conditions are such that it is more convenient to
place the coupler outdoors and run separate lead-in wires into
the house to the individual sets. Fig. 6-9 shows a two-set split-
ter/coupler, but in a weatherproof housing, and with clamps
for fastening it to the mast holding the antenna. A mast-
mounted, four-set coupler is also available.

Similar couplers are available for use with 75-ohm coaxial
cable. The difference is only in the method of termination on
the boxes. Small coaxial cable jacks are used instead of screw
terminals. The cables must have mating plugs connected to
their ends. Also, each tv set must have a transformer on the
back, at the terminals, to change 75 ohms to the 300-ohm input impedance of the tv set.

In small apartment buildings, up to eight sets may be fed
with the same antenna. One two-set and two four-set couplers
can be connected into a distribution system as shown in Fig. 6-
10. Since you will be dividing the available power by eight, a

Fig. 6-9. Two-set splitter/coupler.

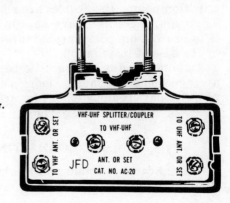

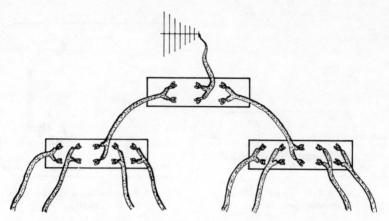

Fig. 6-10. Two-set coupler feeding into two four-set couplers.

good antenna must be put up and installed as high above the roof as practical.

AMPLIFIED SYSTEMS

In larger apartment buildings, and in hotels and motels, an amplified system is required. Specially designed amplifiers build up the signal from the antenna and make it possible to feed a very large number of sets. While the amplifiers are powered by the ac lines, they are designed to draw very little current from the line, and may run 24 hours a day at low cost. Thy are transistorized and may run for years without need for service.

Usual practice is to install an amplifier right at the antenna, between the antenna terminals and the lead-in. The lead-in carries the tv signal down and power from a small power supply up to the amplifier. Additional amplifiers are placed at distribution points, then cables are run from them to the tv sets. These amplifiers also have built-in couplers. General practice is to use 75-ohm coaxial cable throughout the system, because of the ease of installation.

Amplified systems are a little beyond the capabilities of the average home mechanic. Their installation is best left to the professional organizations, who are better equipped with the necessary tools and knowledge.

INTERCONNECTING CABLE

Coaxial cable is round and small in diameter. Running the cable from antenna to coupler to sets poses no problems. However, it is expensive, and there is a need to install plugs onto the ends of the cables.

Three hundred-ohm twin lead distribution is less expensive than coaxial cable, and connecting them to couplers and tv sets is a simpler job. It is only necessary to strip a little insulation off the ends and wrap the wires around the screw terminals and tighten down on the screws. Some couplers even have claw-like washers under the screw heads which bite down through the insulation and eliminate the job of stripping. This is not true at the tv set terminals, however.

The only precaution that must be observed in running twin-lead cable around is to avoid coming near large amounts of metal. The cable should not be run near or parallel to electric wires, or water or gas pipes. There should be a distance of at least four inches from such metal. Shielded cable eliminates this precaution.

Running twin lead around the wall molding is fairly easy except when going from one room to another. Running it around door openings poses a problem and requires a little ingenuity. Special tacks are available to hold the cable in place against the floor molding. Since some 300-ohm cable is either white in color, or clear, there usually is no problem of wall color matching.

The best way to feed cable to the sets is through the wall, and is fairly easy in a one-story home with an attic. The lead-in may be brought into the attic from the antenna either directly through the roof, or around over the edge of the roof overhang (or via the basement or crawl space). The coupler is fastened to the top of a ceiling joist, or to a roof rafter. Or it may be just laid on top of a ceiling joist without fastening. Nothing will disturb it. The cables to the individual sets are dropped through a hole in the wall plate to a point in the wall near the set.

The inner walls of nearly all homes have 2 × 4 studs between the plaster boards. No insulation is used in the inner walls and,

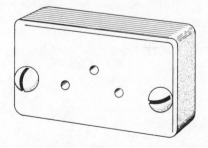

Fig. 6-11. Antenna outlet.

usually, there is no obstruction to dropping the cable to a point about a foot above the floor line. In some cities the fire codes require firebreaks (fire stops) in walls. These are horizontal pieces of 2 × 4 studs about halfway up the wall. Going through these poses a problem. If your home has a basement or crawl space, coming in from below avoids the firebreak pieces.

The best way to do an in-the-wall installation is at the time the home is being build. Just before the plaster walls go up is an ideal time to get in and run the cable.

Fish the cable through a hole cut into the plaster near the tv set. A better way is to install a tv antenna outlet (Fig. 6-11).

CHAPTER 7

HOW TO INSTALL A TV ANTENNA

Television antennas are really quite easy to install. They are made so by most manufacturers of tv antennas, and it is especially true of the Archer line, sold exclusively by Radio Shack.

When you buy an antenna, the package you get is much smaller than the antenna. This is because the long elements on the antenna are folded flat against the boom, like the wings of a bird folded against its body. Fig. 7-1 shows an Archer antenna being pulled out of its box. Its elements are folded to make a compact box fit. In Fig. 7-2 the antenna is being prepared for installation. Two pairs of elements have been unfolded; the other pair is still folded. No tools are needed to ready the antenna for installation. The elements are unfolded by hand. Specially designed swivel joints snap the elements into place when they are opened. In fact, it is impossible to refold the elements without damaging them, that's how securely they are held in place. When completely unfolded the antenna looks like Fig. 3-4 in Chapter 3. The elements of the uhf front section are so short they do not need folding, so are fixed in place.

Very complete instructions are supplied for unfolding and installation. While complete, the language is compact and terse, as seen in Fig. 7-3, which shows a copy of the instructions supplied with the antenna mentioned above. Also included with Archer vhf/fm/uhf antennas is a vhf/uhf splitter, the use of which will be covered later.

Fig. 7-1. Packaged tv antenna.

ROOF MOUNTING

The most popular place to mount a tv antenna is on the roof of your home. If you are located close to a tv station, and your house is orientated correctly, the antenna may be mounted in the attic. In deep fringe areas even the roof level of the house may not be high enough, and a high tower or mast is needed. But for average metropolitan and suburban distances, the roof of a home usually provides a good height for the antenna.

In addition to the antenna and a mount, you will need a metal mast, either five feet or ten feet long. These are standard tv items in all stores selling tv antennas.

There is a large variety of hardware items available for mounting an antenna on the roof. One of the sturdiest is the tripod type of mount shown in Fig. 7-4. It is fastened to the peak of the roof as shown in the inset sketch, or onto a flat

Fig. 7-2. Unfolding the antenna elements.

roof. Normally a five-foot mast is fastened to the antenna, and the assembly is inserted through the apex of the tripod and through the center brace, for a two-point hold onto the mast. When purchased, the tripod is in a long, but narrow box, as the center brace folds for easier packaging. The bottom feet are adjustable for slanting to match the roof lines. For greater height, a 10-foot mast may be used in this mount.

The roof mount of Fig. 7-5 has hinged base plates for adjusting to the roof slant. It is built of heavy-gauge material and will support a tv antenna on a 5-ft mast without additional guying. If a 10-ft mast is used, guy wires should be run from about the middle of the mast to guy screw eyes or hooks in the roof.

Both of the above roof mounts are fastened to the roof with long wood or lag screws. The screws must be long enough to go through the shingles, or tar paper, whichever is used, and into the wood below. If possible, find the location of the roof rafters

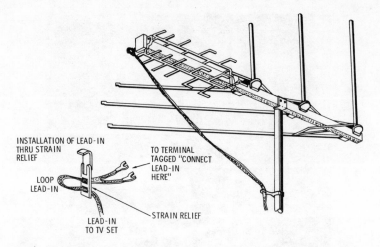

INSTALLATION OF LEAD-IN THRU STRAIN RELIEF

TO TERMINAL TAGGED "CONNECT LEAD-IN HERE"

LOOP LEAD-IN

LEAD-IN TO TV SET

STRAIN RELIEF

1. UNFOLD THE ELEMENTS OF THE ANTENNA AND ATTACH THE ANTENNA TO THE TOP OF THE MAST.

2. AIM THE ANTENNA TOWARD THE DESIRED STATION OR IF A ROTOR IS TO BE USED, FOLLOW THE DIRECTIONS LISTED WITH THE ROTOR. TIGHTEN THE MAST CLAMP.

3. ATTACH THE 300-Ω TWIN-LEAD WIRE TO THE TERMINAL POINTS TAGGED "CONNECT LEAD-IN HERE." IF YOU ARE USING YOUR OLD LEAD-IN WIRE, BE SURE THE INSULATION IS NOT CRACKED OR WEATHERED SO THAT ELECTRICAL BREAKDOWN CAN'T OCCUR. IT IS RECOMMENDED THAT NEW LEAD-IN BE USED WITH ANY NEW ANTENNA INSTALLATION.
LEAD-IN SHOULD BE TWISTED APPROXIMATELY THREE TURNS EVERY 5 FEET.

4. USE SUFFICIENT STANDOFFS ON LEAD-IN TO PREVENT WHIPPING IN THE WIND. STAND-OFFS SHOULD NOT BE MORE THAN 5 FEET APART. WHEN RUNNING LEAD-IN OVER ROOF EDGE OR AROUND OTHER STRUCTURAL PROJECTIONS, PLACE STANDOFFS SO THAT LEAD-IN CLEARS ANY METAL AT LEAST 4 INCHES. RUNNING LEAD-IN THRU OR NEAR ALUMINUM STORM WINDOWS SHOULD BE AVOIDED. SIGNAL LOSS OCCURS ANYWHERE METAL IS CLOSE TO 300-Ω LEAD-IN. DO NOT COIL EXCESS LEAD-IN BEHIND THE TV SET. CUT LEAD-IN SO THAT IT HAS A MINIMUM OF SLACK.

5. RUN A GOOD GROUND WIRE FROM THE ANTENNA MAST TO A GOOD GROUND ROD TO PREVENT LIGHTNING DAMAGE. MAKE SURE ALL ELECTRICAL CONNECTIONS ARE SOLID.

6. THE INCLUDED SIGNAL SPLITTER IS TO BE USED AT THE BACK OF THE TELEVISION SET. CONNECT THE LEAD-IN TO THE TERMINALS ON THE SPLITTER SO MARKED AND THE TWO SETS OF WIRE PAIRS TO THE UHF AND VHF TERMINALS ON THE BACK OF THE TV SET AS INDICATED BY THE MARKINGS. IF YOU WISH TO OPERATE AN FM RECEIVER OFF OF THE ANTENNA, CONNECT THE FM TERMINALS OF THE SPLITTER TO THE FM TERMINALS ON THE BACK OF THE RECEIVER WITH A LENGTH OF 300-Ω TWIN LEAD.

Fig. 7-3. Instructions for installing a tv antenna.

under the wood sheathing beneath the shingles; long screws make a more secure hold when they also grip the roof rafters. Be sure to daub the areas around the screws with an asbestos-filled roof tar. It is available as a patching tar, in quart cans, from most hardware stores and hardware departments of department stores.

Vent pipes are very secure methods of holding a tv antenna mast. Vent pipes are usually four inches in diameter, and extend through the roof from bathrooms, the laundry area, or

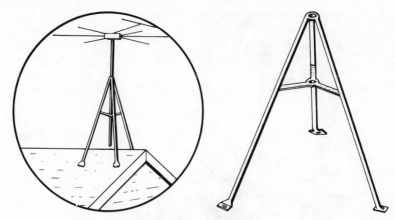

Fig. 7-4. Tripod roof mount.

kitchen. A two-piece clamp for holding the mast is best. This is the type of clamp used to install the antenna shown in Figs. 7-1 and 7-2. Fig. 7-6 shows the bottom of the mast fastened to a vent pipe, using this type of vent clamp. Fig. 7-7 is a view of

Fig. 7-5. Roof peak mount.

Fig. 7-6. Two-piece vent pipe clamp.

the antenna installed and with lead-in connected. The clamps (Fig. 7-6) are each held by a single bolt, and tightening it tightens both the part of the clamp which holds the tv mast and the part which holds to the vent pipe. Mounting is easier if the mast is mounted to the clamp with the antenna off, and the antenna is mounted to the top of the mast after. This can be done by one man if a 5-ft mast is used. Using a 10-ft mast requires mounting the antenna to the mast first, then inserting the whole assembly into the vent mount. This will usually require two men, one to hold the mast and antenna assembly and the other to tighten the mount. Note the mountains in the background view of Fig. 7-7. The tv station antennas are located at the top of the mountain in this city. The antenna has a fortunately good line-of-sight path. The front of the antenna, which

Fig. 7-7. Antenna installed with lead-in connected.

Fig. 7-8. Vhf antenna.

in this case is the end with the uhf section, should point directly to the tv stations' location.

Fig. 7-8 shows a vhf antenna. The city in which this antenna was installed does not have uhf service, and the distance between this home and the tv stations is greater than for the example shown in Fig. 7-7. Therefore, an antenna with more elements and without the uhf section was chosen. The method of mounting is otherwise the same. The end of the antenna with the shorter elements is considered the front, and that is the end that is orientated to point to the tv station location.

Mounting the antenna to the mast is done by means of a U-bolt. The curve of the U goes around the mast, and the double bolt runs through the boom of the antenna. Two nuts with lock washers secure the U-bolt.

Fig. 7-9. Chimney mount.

CHIMNEY MOUNTING

One of the most common methods of mounting a tv antenna is to attach it to the chimney. A number of mounting hardware types are available for this. All use the principle of banding the chimney with stainless steel straps and securing, by means of the bands, the mounting hardware that holds the tv mast.

One of the best chimney mounts is shown in Fig. 7-9. A single strap holds a V-shaped vertical piece to the chimney. The V-shaped part against the chimney corner is .05 inch aluminum. This is fastened to an embossed horizontal section of 12-gauge steel. U-bolts in the horizontal sections hold the tv mast.

Fig. 7-10 shows the popular Z-mount, the separate parts of which are in the photo of Fig. 7-11. A set of two Z-mounts is required to hold a tv mast.

Both of the mounts above use eye-bolts with one side flat to hold the stainless-steel straps. Nuts on the threaded parts of the bolts draw the straps up tight around the chimney.

The ratchet chimney mount of Fig. 7-12 also uses straps around the chimney, but it employs a different method of tightening the straps. A ratchet system, detailed in Fig. 7-13, pulls up tight on the strap when turned by a wrench. The idea is a clever one, and some may think this is an easier method of tightening the straps. The nut method of tightening is a little slower but is just as secure when done.

If the chimney is brick, and it appears that some of the mortar has loosened from aging, it would be best to have it tuckpointed before installing a chimney mount. A poor mortar condition can be made worse from the wind whip on a tv antenna when mounted to the chimney.

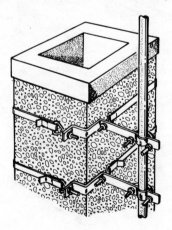

Fig. 7-10. A Z-type chimney mount.

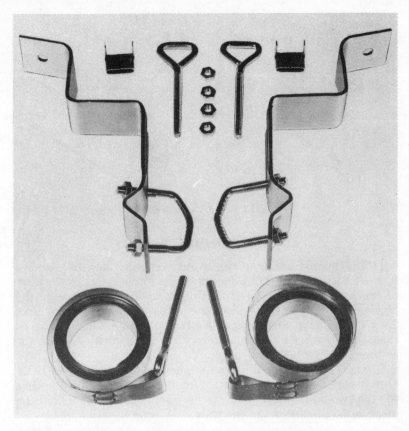

Fig. 7-11. Separate parts of a Z-type chimney mount.

Fig. 7-12. Ratchet chimney mount.

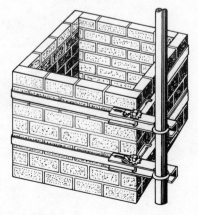

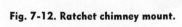

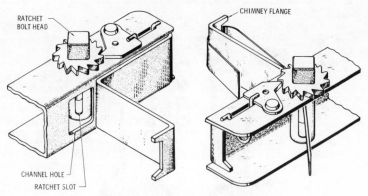

RATCHET
BOLT HEAD

CHIMNEY FLANGE

CHANNEL HOLE

RATCHET SLOT

Fig. 7-13. Ratchet system details.

WALL MOUNTING

If it is desired to mount the tv antenna in a place that makes it the least conspicuous, it should be mounted as far to the rear of the house as possible. Mounting it to the back wall of the house, with a mast that places the antenna above the roof line, does this. There are several wall mounts available, most of them based on the use of brackets with a V or modified U-shape to them.

Fig. 7-14 shows a wall mount. The metal is 3/16 inch thick aluminum. The two brackets are mounted one above the other to give two-point suspension to the mast. The brackets hold the mast out six inches from the wall.

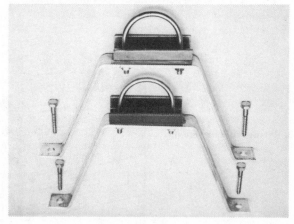

Fig. 7-14. Wall mount.

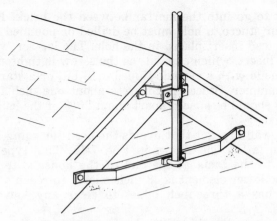

Fig. 7-15. Wall mount for a peak-roofed home.

Heavy-duty wood lag screws are all that are needed for mounting the brackets to the side of a house using wood sheathing. Try to find at least one of the vertical wall studs, and use screws long enough to reach the stud. The next stud would normally be 16 inches away, too far for the other end of the bracket to reach. With most homes built of brick or stucco, wood screws must give way to lag screws. For brick homes, it

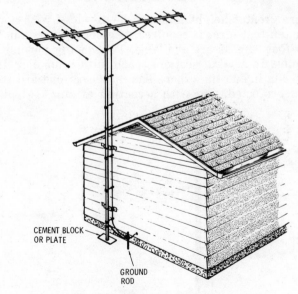

CEMENT BLOCK
OR PLATE

GROUND
ROD

Fig. 7-16. Grounding the mast.

is easier to go into the mortar between the brick. For either mortar or stucco, a hole must be drilled or pounded out and a wood or lead insert placed in the hole. The lag screw is placed into the insert, which expands as the screw is tightened. Holes can be made with a carbide-tipped drill bit, or a star drill and sledge hammer. Stucco is concrete about one inch thick. The brackets should be spaced apart about 20% of the length of the mast used.

A sidewall bracket that avoids the need for going into brick or stucco is the one shown in Fig. 7-15. This type is wood-screwed to the facia at the end of the house with a peaked roof. The lower element is 48 inches long, to reach across. The bracket has a three-inch offset to clear any louvered vent windows.

Mounting to the side of the house has one special advantage in lightning protection. A ground wire can be run straight down to a rod in the ground, providing a short and straight run for best protection. Fig. 7-16 shows the use of a gas or water pipe for a mast, run all the way down to the ground level, where it is connected to a ground rod. The bracket of Fig. 7-14 will take pipes as thick as 2½ inches by omitting the make-up block, as shown in Fig. 7-17.

MAST MOUNTING

Where greater height than can be provided with a standard five- or ten-foot mast is required, telescoping masts in 20-, 30-, and 40-foot lengths are available. Telescoping means the mast is supplied in several sections, each with a smaller diameter, so each fits inside the other. The mast sections are steel, galvanized protected, and with a coating of zinc. In spite of its

MAKE-UP BLOCK

Fig. 7-17. Make-up block.

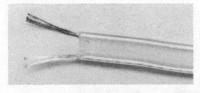 

(A) *Twin lead.*   (B) *Coaxial cable.*

Fig. 7-18. Lead-in cable.

steel construction, the total weight of the 40-foot mast is only 33 lbs.

Because of the greater height of masts, they must be guyed. Guying rings are supplied with the masts, for attaching the guy wires.

Chapter 5 on fringe area antennas covers the raising of masts.

RUNNING THE LEAD-IN

The two principal types of lead-in were discussed in previous chapters. As a review, the two types are shown in Fig. 7-18.

Fig. 7-19. A 300- to 75-ohm transformer and protective boot.

The round, black cable is coaxial 75-ohm cable. The flat-looking wire is 300-ohm twin lead. The coaxial cable features the shielding of one lead with an outer lead of braided wire. This and the fact that it is round makes it easier to run from the antenna to the tv set; it is not affected by nearby wires or noise-producing equipment. The 300-ohm lead-in is also available in a shielded type, but it is more commonly used as shown in the photo.

The antenna installation of Fig. 7-7 shows the coaxial cable used for the lead-in. Because the antenna is designed for 300-ohm lead-in, and the coaxial cable has a characteristic imped-

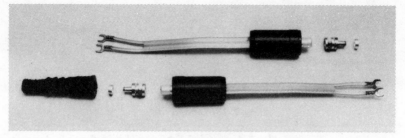

Fig. 7-20. Impedance-matching transformers.

ance of 75 ohms, a transformer must be used to change one impedance to the other. This can be seen in greater detail in the photo of Fig. 7-19. This transformer has a rubber jacket over the cable plug to protect it from moisture. An identical transformer is used at the tv set to change the impedance back from 75 ohms to 300 ohms, the impedance of the tv set input. Being indoors, no rubber jacket is used on the cable plug. The Radio Shack lead-in package consists of a pair of transformers, two plugs for installing onto the cable, and one rubber jacket. It includes instructions for installing the plugs on the cable. The complete set is pictured in Fig. 7-20.

Fig. 7-21 is a closeup view of a plug installed onto the coaxial cable. Some of the outer rubber cover is cut away. Then the shielding is cut away, followed by some of the inner insulation between the inner conductor and shielding. This is shown somewhat exaggeratedly in Fig. 7-21. A ring-shaped ferrule supplied with the plug is slipped over the cable. The neck of the plug is slipped between the braided shield and the inner insulation, the ferrule is moved down over the braided wires and crimped tight with some pliers. This makes connection between the shell of the plug and the shield. The inner

Fig. 7-21. Coaxial plug.

conductor fits through a small hole in the plug and protrudes slightly out the front. The wire itself becomes the center pin of the plug.

On 300-ohm twin lead, some of the insulation is stripped away from the two wires, exposing about ¾ inch of wires. Twist the wires in the direction in which they are normally twisted in the cable, and bend a hook on both of them. Hook the wires under the screws at the antenna and at the tv set and tighten down on the screws.

Both types of lead-in must be supported every few feet with standoff insulators, to prevent their being whipped by the wind, and, in the case of the 300-ohm twin lead, to keep it away from metals. In addition, the 300-ohm lead must be twisted about five turns every yard. This gives equal capacity effect exposure to any metals that may be nearby, and maintains a balanced condition in the two wires.

STANDOFFS

Different standoffs are used for fastening to different types of structures. The photographs that follow show them. However, the black circular part of the insulators are all the same

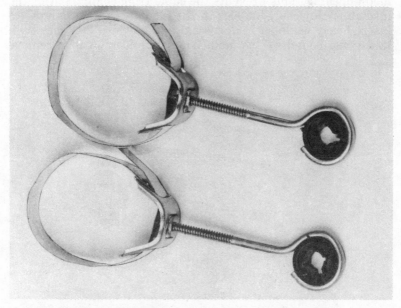

Fig. 7-22. Standoff insulators using stainless steel straps.

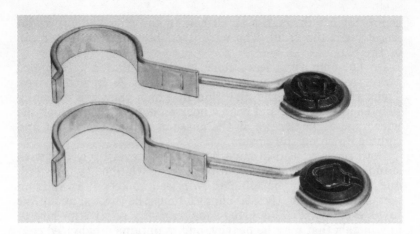

Fig. 7-23. Standoff insulators using hook snaps.

and are designed to take any kind of cable. They are slotted on one side, and they turn in the metal part that encircles and holds them. The cables are attached by turning the insulator to where the slot is in line with the open part of the metal, and the cable is forced into the center through the slot. After the cable is in, the insulator is turned so the slot is opposite the metal opening. This prevents the cable from coming out of the insulator. However, the slot in the insulator is too narrow to insert heavy cable such as coaxial and shielded 300-ohm twin lead while bound by the metal ring. For heavy cable, remove

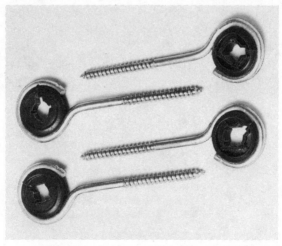

Fig. 7-24. Standoff insulators using wood screws.

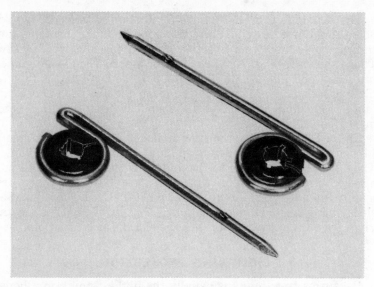

Fig. 7-25. Nail-in, standoff insulators for wood.

the insulator by pressing it out, then insert the cable into the insulator, and reinstall it into the ring of the metal holder.

The standoffs in Fig. 7-22 are for mast mounting. They are also shown in Figs. 7-7 and 7-8. The straps on the standoffs are of stainless steel and are fastened at one end. The strap is placed around the mast, and the other end threaded through slots in the base of the standoff. Tightening down on the screws tightens the strap. Another mast type standoff is shown in Fig. 7-23. The hooked part is spring steel and merely snaps onto the mast.

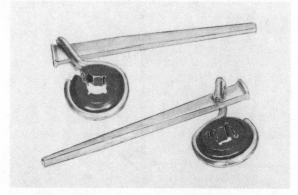

Fig. 7-26. Nail-in, standoff insulators for mortar.

The standoffs in Fig. 7-24 are for fastening to wood. A pilot hole should first be drilled into the wood, to make inserting and tightening easier. This practice is good for any wood screw. Those shown in Fig. 7-25 are also for wood. They are pounded into the wood like a nail. Note the reverse bend at the top for taking the hammer blows. A crimp on the shank, a short distance from the point, makes a firmer fit when the nail is hammered home.

Fig. 7-26 shows mortar-type nails as part of the standoff. Like any mortar nails, they have blunt ends and square shanks. They are easily driven into the mortar between bricks and will also go through concrete, with extra care. But they are primarily intended for fastening into mortar. Use a short-handled sledge hammer and drive them firmly but carefully. The mortar gives way and compacts around the shank for a firm hold.

LIGHTNING PROTECTION

Because a tv antenna is usually the highest point on a house it could be struck by lightning if allowed to stand and accumulate a static charge. During a thunderstorm static can accumulate. The chances of lightning striking the antenna are considerably reduced if the static charge is drained off. This is done by grounding the antenna. If by chance lightning should strike the antenna, the charge will be carried to the ground on the outside of the house instead of through the house. Furthermore, most insurance codes require that tv antennas be grounded.

Fig. 7-27. Grounding bar.

Grounding merely means running a wire from the mast of the antenna to a rod driven into the ground.

Large conductor wire should be used for the ground wire. It need not be copper, although copper is preferred. The usual type of ground wire is aluminum, only because it is much more easily handled in the large sizes.

Loosen one of the bolts that support the mast and hook the ground wire around it. Tighten the bolt again. Run the wire over the roof and down the side of the house along the shortest path between mast and ground. Drive a metal rod into the earth (Fig. 7-27) and twist the other end of the wire around it near the top. If copper wire is used, it may be soldered to the rod with a blow torch and resin-core solder (never use acid-core solder for electrical connections), as was done in the photo of Fig. 7-27. If aluminum wire is used, purchase a special clamp, any one of the many types will do. The clamps are similar to those used by electricians or telephone installers for grounding wires to water pipes.

Ground rods should be six or eight feet in length. The best ones are steel with a copper-clad overall. One end is tapered for easy driving. In areas where the soil is hard and dry you may need to place a hose at the location and let a trickle of water run for a while to soften the earth enough for driving the rod into it. Dry soil is not a good electrical conductor, but it becomes wet in a rain storm and will then make a good soil for lightning protection.

RUNNING LEAD-IN INDOORS

If the lead-in cannot be brought through the attic and down an inner wall, as shown in the photo of Fig. 7-28, the next best

Fig. 7-28. Coaxial lead-in entering an attic.

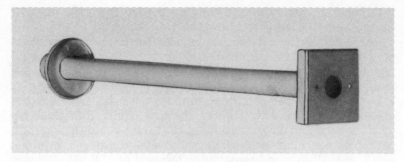

thing is to go through the outside wall of the house. This is done by means of a "wall tube," as illustrated in Fig. 7-29. This feed-through type of device is all plastic, takes any kind of lead-in, and will fit walls up to 13 inches thick. It includes a rubber grommet for the outside flange, which makes the fit weatherproof.

If the outside wall is brick, select a point at a corner of the bricks and pound a hole through the mortar with a star drill. If your home is frame and veneer brick (one thickness of brick), determine where a stud in the wall is by means of a magnetic device to identify plaster-holding nails in the studs. These magnetic detectors are inexpensive and may be purchased at any hardware outlet. When going through the mortar between the brick, select a point that won't strike a stud inside. An all-brick home will have two or more thicknesses of brick, and ¾ inch furring strips between the brick and plaster walls. A star drill will go through the furring strip without trouble.

The inside end of the wall tube is made to accommodate the wall socket illustrated in Fig. 7-30. Thread the 300-ohm twin lead through the wall tube, fasten it to the terminals of the socket, and fasten the socket to the wall tube. No soldering is required.

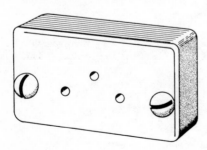

Fig. 7-30. Wall tube socket.

A mating plug, supplied with the socket mentioned above, is then connected to a 300-ohm twin lead long enough to reach the tv set. The plug, also, requires no soldering. If the tv set is not near the socket, you may find it necessary to run twin lead along the molding to the location of the tv set. Special tacks are available to do this, and the installation is quite inconspicuous.

If the lead-in can be brought through the attic and down a wall, the installation can be much more professional looking. There is more work involved, however. The work has to do with dropping the cable down inside the wall.

The inside walls of homes are usually made of 2 × 4 studding with plaster board fastened to both sides. Across the top of the studs are one or two thicknesses of 2 × 4 called a plate. On inspection you will see electrical conduit, or unpiped electrical cable, going through places in the plate that are exposed in the attic. If you are using coaxial cable, or shielded 300-ohm line, you can thread your cable through the same cuts in the plate as the other services, and there is usually enough extra room to do this. For unshielded 300-ohm line you must drill a new hole and keep the line away from any other cables or metallic objects.

Some city codes require home construction to include firebreaks in the walls. These are horizontal pieces of 2 × 4 set in about halfway down the wall. If these are present in your walls, you have a problem. The only way to go through these firebreak pieces is to drop a weighted string down the hole in the plate and estimate the distance down for the firebreak piece. Then, chop some plaster away inside the room at the point where the firebreak is, notch the wood to allow the cable to go around it, and replaster and repaint the wall.

Homes with basements or crawl spaces under them can use the method described above, but working up from the space beneath, through the sill on which the studs rest. The sill is similar in construction to the plate mentioned. Where firebreaks are used in walls, working from a crawl space or basement beneath avoids the problem, as it is only necessary to go about a foot above the molding.

The lead-in may be brought through a wall by cutting a small hole just large enough to accommodate the cable. Estimate the entrance to be as near to your tv set as possible. A preferable method is to install an electrical box and use a socket wall plate, described below. Electrical boxes are available for support by the plaster will itself, as well as by nailing to studs.

If you are planning on building, or are in the process of building a new home, the time to put in tv cables is when the house is fully framed, but before the plaster walls have been installed. The work of running cable in the wall is very easy at that time.

WALL MOUNTING SOCKETS

A neat indoor lead-in installation is the end result when cables are run in the wall and terminated in a wall mounting socket. The finished look is like that of an ac outlet of your house wiring system. Fig. 7-31 shows one of several plates available. Some fit the standard electrical outlet boxes, as mentioned above. Others are made for surface mounting onto the wall, and no box is needed behind them. The one in Fig. 7-31

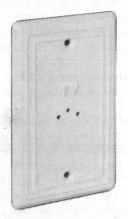 

Fig. 7-31. Wall plate receptacle for twin-lead cable.   Fig. 7-32. Wall plate receptacle for coaxial cable.

is for box mounting, which puts the plate flush against the wall. This one is made to accommodate a matching plug, for use with one 300-ohm twin line. Another has two sets of terminal holes for taking two plugs, for use either when two separate antennas and lines are used, one for vhf and one for uhf (most tv sets have separate input terminals for vhf and for uhf), or for a single line with a splitter mounted behind the plate.

Some plates have terminal combinations for connecting a tv set and a multicable line to a rotor. Matching plugs are available for both.

Fig. 7-32 is a photograph of an actual installation of a plate with coaxial cable termination. The wall is too light in color to be recognized as a wall. The type of plug shown in Fig. 7-21 screws into the receptacle.

CONNECTING THE TV SET

The point where the lead-in is brought into the house should be as close to the tv set as possible. Whether it is terminated in a wall socket, or brought through the wall in a continuous piece, the lead-in must finally end at the tv set.

If a wall plate is used, a length of cable just long enough to run from the wall to the tv set must be made up. The wall plate has a three-hole socket for each tv set. The mating plug for it has three pins in the form of a triangle. The two wires of a length of twin lead are connected to the two pins farthest apart. The third pin merely adds a better grip to the plug when in the socket. Skin the insulation off the two wires far enough to permit inserting the wires into the pins so they will reach a little beyond the location of the side screws. Insert the wires and tighten the screws.

At the other end of the cable, the insulation is skinned from the two wires and fastened to the screw terminals on the back of the tv set. Twist the wires in the direction of their natural twist, and place them around the terminals in a clockwise direction, then tighten down on the screws.

Color sets usually have two sets of terminals, one for vhf and one for uhf. A splitter must be used to divide the signal between the two inputs. One is furnished with all Archer vhf/fm/uhf antennas, or it may be purchased separately. Splitters have two short stubs of twin lead, each ending in spade lugs. One is marked for the vhf input on the tv set, and one is marked for the uhf input. At least one set of screw terminals is on the case, for the main tv lead-in cable.

CHAPTER 8

INDOOR TV ANTENNAS

It is a long road from the days of the simple rabbit ear antenna for indoor use, to today's multiple-tuned indoor antenna. Time was when the only tv stations on the air were in Channels 2 to 13, the vhf section of tv channels. And before the days of color tv, the simple rabbit ear with its telescoping elements did a pretty good job in locations where outdoor antennas were impossible. Sliding the elements in and out tuned the antenna to the channels in use.

DESIGN FOR TODAY'S TV

The evolution in the design of indoor antennas for tv follows the evolution of the increased services offered by tv. When uhf channels came into use, the simple rabbit ears were not adequate. The elements were too long to resonate at the much higher frequency channels. The rabbit ears were maintained for the vhf section of the band, but elements were added for uhf, and they were made tunable. Fig. 8-1 illustrates one of the simplest of these. The large hairpin shaped element in the center was made tunable by a front knob and is resonated to the uhf channels. With resonance came proper impedance match, and better overall results. Fig. 8-2 shows another form of a similar antenna, using a double loop for the uhf channels. Each have separate lines for connecting to the vhf and uhf terminals of the tv set.

Fig. 8-3 shows another indoor antenna for tv. It looks similar to those described above, but has improvements over them. The vhf elements and uhf loops are mounted on a rotating

Fig. 8-1. Indoor antenna with tunable
uhf hairpin loop.

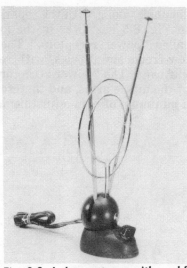

Fig. 8-2. Indoor antenna with a uhf
double loop.

turntable for easy adjustment. The antenna has a uhf-vhf-fm
selector and a phasing switch for fine tuning.

Figs. 8-4 and 8-5 are similar except for the special loading
coils on the vhf elements of Fig. 8-5. Note the more elaborate
uhf loops, the use of which gives better coverage of all uhf

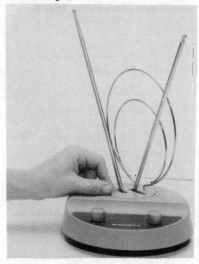

Fig. 8-3. Indoor antenna with a
rotating turntable.

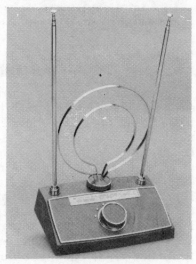

Fig. 8-4. An indoor antenna without
loading coils.

channels, along with the separate tuning controls. The antenna in Fig. 8-5 has discs in the low-frequency dipoles, which are called "power receptors." They add to the inductance of the low-frequency dipoles, with resulting better resonance in the vhf band. The "power receptors" electrically extend the length of the dipole arms, and therefore provide better reception with a minimum of arm adjustments.

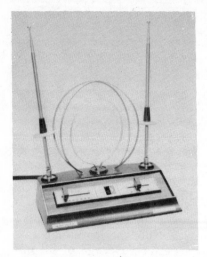

Fig. 8-5. "Power receptor" in the elements give better vhf results.

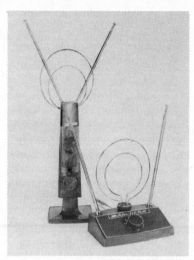

Fig. 8-6. Indoor rotating television antennas.

SPECIAL ANTENNAS FOR COLOR

The indoor tv antennas described above will work well with color sets under close-in conditions, and where an outdoor antenna is out of the question. For better pickup they may be manually rotated. This requires turning the entire antenna. To be able to rotate the antenna portion only, and not the base, is an added feature of the following tv antennas.

In Fig. 8-6 the antenna in front has a rotatable uhf section. It has the usual four section vhf dipoles and tuning device for the uhf section, like those described above. The rear antenna in the photograph has a tower-like construction which gives added height to the antenna elements and introduces a distinctively new style. The top section rotates both the vhf and the uhf sections of the antenna. The long vhf elements fold down when they are not in use.

AN "ULTIMATE" INDOOR TV ANTENNA

The antenna previously pictured in Fig. 3-18 has a six-section vhf elements, plus the "power receptor" loading discs. The uhf section has two fixed loops and one rotatable loop. Its rotation is controlled by a knob on the front panel. In addition, uhf is tuned from the front panel. An interference rejection filter is built in. For the family with a color set, and who wants the best possible results from an indoor tv antenna, this antenna represents today's ultimate design.

A weak signal on a black and white set may introduce some "snow" in the picture. The enjoyment factor is not too affected by this. However, a weak color signal to a color set causes loss of color, or a change of color. This is quite intolerable for the full enjoyment of color programs. Good color reception can be assured with the proper outdoor antenna. However, where circumstances prevent the use of an outdoor antenna, it is worth the set user's extra dollars to invest in the best possible indoor antenna. After all, the investment in the color set represents quite a considerable sum in itself.

Having purchased an indoor antenna it is wise to do some experimenting for best results. Experiment with locations in the room. The top of the tv set might seem to be the most convenient place for the antenna, but it is not necessarily the best place. An outdoor antenna has high forward directivity and reduces the possibility of "ghosts" or secondary images. An indoor antenna does not have this quality. Ghosts may be introduced by the return bounce of a secondary path signal from metallic objects in the room. If you encounter ghosts in the picture, move the antenna to another location. Try another, and still another. Find the spot that gives you the fewest ghosts, and the best hold to color pictures.

FM INDOOR ANTENNAS

Like tv, the best reception on a fm tuner or receiver is from an outdoor antenna. Next best is from a two-set coupler connected to a tv antenna, where the coupler feeds the tv set and the fm tuner.

The frequency range of fm is 88 to 108 MHz. Being only 20 MHz wide, it does not compare with the broad frequency spectrum of tv. For this reason many fm tuners are supplied with an indoor dipole made of 300-ohm twin line, like the one described in the chapter on fm antennas. While they work quite well they still cannot cover the full 20-MHz frequency width with equal response across the entire band. Nor can they be turned for best pickup if fm stations are in different directions, which is generally the case. The fm indoor antenna previously shown in Fig. 4-8, overcomes the two shortcomings mentioned above. The telescoping elements and tuned coil in the center provide precise tuning to the frequency to be received. In addition, the antenna can be turned on its base for best directivity.

As in the case of the color-tv reception, a stereo signal requires the reception of a much stronger signal for the multiplex control carrier to give good stereo separation. A tunable indoor antenna, such as this one, can give good stereo reception, short of an outdoor antenna.

CHAPTER 9

INSTALLING A ROTATOR

There are a number of advantages in using a rotator for a tv antenna. In fringe area reception, where the location may be between two cities with tv service, the advantage of being able to turn the tv antenna in the direction of either city is an obvious one. In such fringe area locations, no antenna installation should be contemplated without including a rotator.

Even in close-in metropolitan or suburban areas, there may be an advantage to the use of a rotator, depending on circumstances. In some cities not all tv stations are located in the same place. While the practice is for all stations to work together and all place their antennas on a single high point, this practice is not universal. Where this is not the case, the use of a rotator is a necessity, if best reception is desired from all stations.

Whether all tv station antennas are in the same place or not, there is almost always the problem of secondary paths, which result in ghosts in the picture. A highly directional receiving antenna should eliminate or substantially reduce the strength of the secondary path signal. But where this is not possible, a rotator can be the answer. A rotator can orient your antenna just enough in one direction or the other to turn it away from the secondary path signal, yet not lose enough primary path signal strength to affect reception. The proper use of a rotator can completely eliminate the ghost.

Fm station antennas are hardly ever located in one place. If fm reception is as important to you as the reception of tv, include a rotator in your installation if for no other purpose than to turn your tv antenna (it is assumed you are feeding both tv and fm tuner from the same antenna) in the direction of the fm transmitting antenna location. This is important to the best reception of stereo fm.

MANUAL AND AUTOMATIC ROTATORS

There are two basic types of rotator systems, manual and automatic. Each system consists of a rotating mechanism with an electric motor and reduction gears in a weatherproof housing, and a control box and indicator. The mechanism is located on top of the mast, and above it the antenna is mounted. The indicator is located in the house, on or near the tv set. A four- or five-wire cable connects the two.

On manual rotator systems, the indicator has a lever or switch and a meter marked with compass points instead of numbers. The lever or switch is pressed in one direction or the other and held while watching the meter. When the needle on the meter shows the direction you want, the lever is released. On automatic systems, a knob on the control box is set to the

Fig. 9-1. Automatic rotator.

direction desired. The turning mechanism rotates the antenna until its direction matches the setting on the knob, then it stops.

The two Archer rotators pictured in this chapter are both automatic types. Both have knobs to set for the direction desired. In either unit the motor starts up and turns the antenna to the direction to which the knob has been set. Both include braking systems to hold the antenna in its set direction.

The rotator shown in Fig. 9-1 uses mechanical braking to hold the mechanism in its stopped position. The mechanism is held in a fixed position to the lower mast with two sets of bolts and serrated clamps (similar to the mechanism mounting shown in Fig. 9-2). The bearings are fully weatherproof and lubricated for life. The control box contains the control dial and solid-state circuitry for handling the control of the motor. The antenna may be turned in either direction but never more than a complete 360° circle. It uses four-wire control cable.

Fig. 9-2 pictures the Archer Servo-Rotor model rotator. It is a heavy-duty mechanism, husky enough to handle most applications. It is designed to accept upper mast sections of any size between 1½ and 2⅛ inches in diameter. The mast fits through the rotating bearing and is held in place by two clamps, one above and one below the mast section. A servomotor with dynamic clutch action is enclosed in the weatherproof housing. The control box has the direction control knob, solid-state amplifier, and includes lights which show the direction of rotation (Fig. 9-3). Just set the control knob to any position and the servomotor takes over. This rotor uses a five-wire control cable.

Fig. 9-2. Archer Servo-Rotor.

Fig. 9-3. Servo-Rotor control box.

CONNECTING THE CONTROL CABLE

The interconnecting control cable may be four-wire, or five-wire, depending on the rotator you purchase. In either case, one outside lead will have a means of identifying it from the others to assure that the wires are connected in proper order at both the mechanism and the control box. Skin back the insulation from each wire at one end. You will probably find that one wire has tin-plated strands of fine wire, and all others are plain copper.

Check the instructions received with the rotator to determine if the tin-plated lead is No. 1, or the highest number. Remove the weatherproof cover on the rotator. Under the cover is a row of screw terminals. Skin the insulation from the several wires in the control cable and wrap one around each terminal, observing the number order given in the instructions. Wrap the wires around the terminals in a clockwise manner. Tighten down on the screws and replace the cover.

At the control box end, cut off excess cable and skin back the insulation of the individual wires. Connect them to the control box terminals in the same order and the same manner as for the rotator mechanism.

The control cable may be dressed close to the mast and taped to it at intervals down its length. No special precautions are required to keep this cable away from metallic objects (except 300-ohm unshielded twin line). If the antenna cable is coaxial or if the 300-ohm cable is shielded, the control cable may be brought down and into the house along with and parallel to the shielded antenna cable. They may be taped together if that is convenient.

The unshielded, ribbon-like, 300-ohm twin line must not be run near the control cable, or any other cable or metallic material. This type of antenna lead-in must be brought down the mast using mast-mounted standoff insulators and carried down and into the house as described before.

ORIENTATING FOR DIRECTION

It is obvious that the antenna must point in the direction to which the control knob has been set. This is easy to achieve.

With the control unit wired to the cable, and the antenna and rotor installed, set the control knob to north. Return to the antenna installation and loosen either the bolts to the antenna or the bolts holding the rotor to the lower mast. Turn one or the other to point to the north, and retighten all bolts.

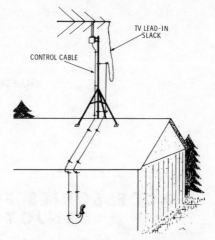

CONTROL CABLE

TV LEAD-IN
SLACK

**Fig. 9-4. Allowing sufficient slack
in the tv cable.**

CAUTION. The antenna lead-in cable must be given enough slack to allow the antenna to turn through a half-circle (180°) in either direction. The rotator does not turn the antenna continuously, but through a circle of 360° and back again. By securing the antenna lead-in at the half-circle point, only a half-circle slack need be allowed.

With the antenna turned to point south, fasten the standoff insulators on the south side of the mast. Allow a loop of cable above the highest mounted standoff, leaving a generous amount of slack. As the antenna rotates to the north in either direction, the slack will be taken up, although it should not pull tight. Fig. 9-4 shows how to do this.

CHAPTER 10

ACCESSORIES FOR BETTER TV ENJOYMENT

One of the first things that comes to mind for increasing enjoyment of tv is to connect more than one tv set to a single tv antenna. This was rather fully covered in Chapter 6, including sketches on how to hook them up.

Fig. 6-9 in Chapter 6 shows a mast-mounted splitter, described in that chapter for use in connecting one antenna to two tv sets, but with the splitter located outside on the mast. Splitters and couplers are transformers and may be operated in reverse, as well as in the way described in Chapter 6. The splitter referred to above may be used in another way. Assume you have a vhf antenna because only stations in the vhf channels were in service. Now, a uhf station or two has been added to your city. You can enjoy uhf service without scrapping the old vhf antenna. Just add a uhf front section, like one of those shown in Chapter 3 (Fig. 3-5). Bring a 300-ohm twin lead down to the mast-mounted splitter and connect it to one end pair of terminals, connect the vhf lead to the other end terminals, and connect the original 300-ohm lead to the center pair of terminals. The splitter has allowed you to add a uhf section and bring both vhf and uhf signals down the same lead-in. Fig. 10-1 shows a sketch of the hookup.

Remember, another splitter will be needed in most cases at the tv set. Most tv sets have two independent sets of terminals for the antenna lead-in connections, one for vhf and one for uhf. A splitter, like the one shown in Fig. 10-2, will divide the signal from the one lead-in into two signals for the two sets of terminals.

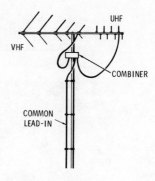

Fig. 10-1. Adding a uhf antenna to a vhf antenna.

UHF CONVERTERS

If your set is one of the older types without the uhf bands on it, it will not receive uhf stations even with the proper antenna. But you can enjoy the new uhf service by adding a uhf converter.

The uhf converter changes the uhf station to vhf for use by your tv set. The converter is designed to convert any chan-

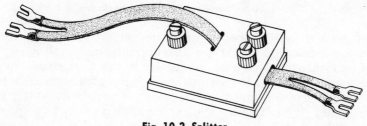

Fig. 10-2. Splitter.

nel to which it is tuned, to either Channel 5 or 6, whichever is not in use in your city. It has all solid-state circuitry, including a uhf preamplifier before the converter stage, to improve sensitivity.

Fig. 10-3 shows a uhf converter. Fig. 10-4 shows a rear

Fig. 10-3. Uhf converter.

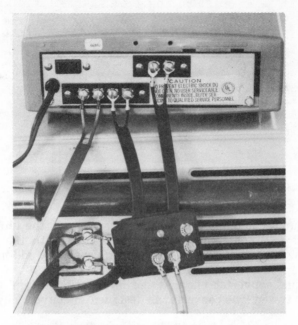

Fig. 10-4. Rear view of converter hookup.

view with a splitter hooked up to the converter. This splitter was furnished with the Archer vhf/uhf antenna installed. Both vhf and uhf signals are fed separately to the converter. When the converter is off, the vhf leads are connected internally to the output which connects to the tv set. When the converter is on, the uhf input from the splitter, connected to the two upper terminals, is converted to a vhf signal and fed to the tv set. The sketches of Fig. 10-5, A through D, show the four ways in which the converter may be used with different antenna systems. Illustration B uses the same antenna system as illustration D, but with separate lead-ins. In D, a common lead-in may be used by adding a mast-mounted coupler (splitter or combiner) such as described previously.

With the converter hooked up and on, and the tv set channel selector on Channel 5 or 6, turn the large knob on the converter until a uhf station is received. The knob on the left of the two smaller knobs is mechanically linked to the large knob and is a fine tuner. It moves the large knob over just a few degrees of rotation.

Fig. 10-6 shows the converter connected to a portable 17-inch tv set. A uhf loop antenna, furnished with the converter, is shown in use. If you are close to a uhf station, this antenna

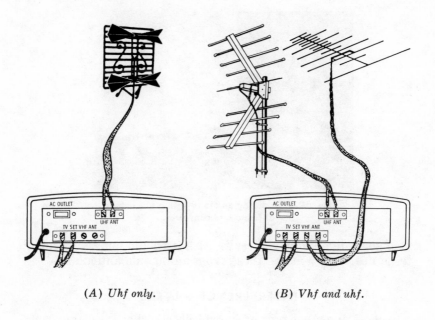

(A) Uhf only.   (B) Vhf and uhf.

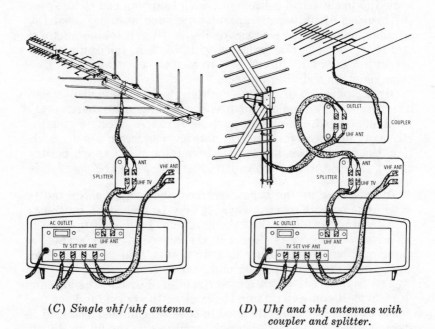

(C) Single vhf/uhf antenna.   (D) Uhf and vhf antennas with
                                     coupler and splitter.

Fig. 10-5. Converter installations.

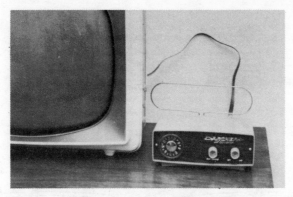

Fig. 10-6. Updating an old tv with a uhf indoor
antenna and converter.

may serve temporarily. Results with it should not be expected
to be nearly as good as those from an outside antenna.

INTERFERENCE FILTERS

A most annoying type of interference is that resulting from
sparking in electrical equipment. Such sparking can come from
the brushes of universal type motors, such as those used for
circular hand saws, electric drills, sewing machine motors,
etc. It will look like a series of white dots in horizontal lines
across a black and white tv set. In a color set, it may look like
colored dots in a similar pattern.

Other sparking of an intermittent nature can also cause
interference. The make and break of contacts in thermostat-
ically controlled equipment, such as furnaces, electric ranges,
etc., can cause occasional bright dots on the screen, usually each
time the contact breaks. This is because a slight spark occurs
across the contacts of the control element when the current is
broken.

Interference of the type described above may enter the tv
set in one or both of two ways. It may be picked up by the ac
line feeding power to the set, or it may be picked up by the
antenna, whichever is closest to the source of interference. A
filter may be used at either or both points, that will bypass all
or most of the spark pickup and keep it from getting into the
tv set. Fig. 10-7 is an antenna-type filter. For use, the antenna
lead-in is disconnected from the back of the tv set, and the two
leads of the filter are connected to the tv terminals. The lead-in
is connected to the pair of screw terminals on the filter. Within
the filter is a bandpass circuit that blocks out all radio fre-

Fig. 10-7. A tv interference filter (antenna).

quencies above and below the tv frequencies, but allows tv
frequencies to pass through. Since interference sparking is at
radio frequencies, those that fall within the tv frequencies will
get through. However, quite a bit of the spark interference will
be blocked, with a resulting decrease in interference.

CHAPTER 11

CB ANTENNAS

All antennas must meet certain basic requirements, regardless of their use. Such basics as the need for resonance, impedance matching, proper feedline, and good construction are common to all. Even expensive broadcast antennas must meet these requirements.

That does not mean all antennas are alike; far from it. The CB antenna is quite different in many details from tv receiving antennas. A CB antenna is resonant to a very narrow band of frequencies. It is designed to receive and transmit. As a transmitting antenna, the legal transmitter power-input limit (five watts) is so small that not a bit can be wasted.

It is standard for the radio waves in the CB band to be vertically polarized. This means that both transmitting and receiving antennas are mounted vertically (unlike tv antennas, whose elements are parallel with the plane of the earth's surface).

One advantage of vertically polarized antennas is a better radiation pattern. A horizontal half-wave antenna has a figure 8 pattern (as described in Chapter 4 on tv antennas). A vertical antenna has a doughnut-shaped pattern and is therefore omnidirectional and has a low angle of radiation. This is ideal for communicating to all directions.

ANTENNA RESONANCE

An antenna is resonant to a radio frequency when its length is one-half the wavelength of that radio wave. Dividing 300 by the frequency in megahertz and dividing again by two will give the length in meters for a resonant antenna. The CB band extends from 26.965 MHz to 27.255 MHz, for 23 channels of operation. The center of the band is about 27.1 MHz. In the above formula a half-wave antenna is about 17½ feet, after converting meters to feet. If you hold a 17½-foot rod vertically in the air, you will have a half-wave antenna resonant in the CB band.

But a straight rod 17½ feet long is hard to mount. Such an antenna would require a long, horizontal support at the middle of the antenna to hold it out so there would be no capacity effect to the mast. It might look something like Fig. 11-1. However there is a more practical approach. By bending the lower element half out and adding two more elements angled the

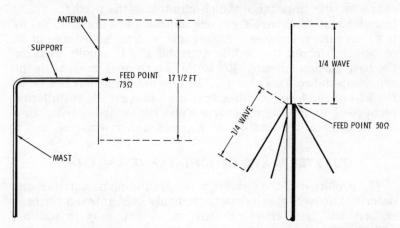

Fig. 11-1. An impractical 17½-ft half-wave antenna.

Fig. 11-2. Diagram of a ground-plane antenna (quarter-wavelength).

same, we have what is called a *ground-plane* antenna, and one that can be mounted with the mast attached to the center (Fig. 11-2). The vertical portion is a quarter-wave long, and the lower radials are each a quarter-wave long. Altogether they make a half-wave antenna.

The above may be compared to broadcast station antennas. Because of the low frequencies of the broadcast band, only a quarter-wave mast is raised, and quarter-wave radial wires are buried in the ground, radiating out from the base of the antenna.

Another example of this is the mobile CB antenna. Its visible section is a quarter-wavelength in height. The car body is a random length quarter-wave for the other half of the antenna. The car body becomes part of the antenna system.

FEEDING AND IMPEDANCE MATCHING

The center of a normal half-wave antenna is theoretically about 73 ohms. When the lower half is bent out, and the other elements added, the center impedance becomes more nearly 50 ohms. The center of the antenna is where it is fed energy from the transmitter, or from which the energy is taken for the receiver. It is electrically and mechanically a more convenient place to make the feedline connection.

Coaxial cable is always used for the feedline, because it has the advantage of the shielded cover which makes it easier to handle. Two types of cable are available with the proper characteristic impedance which eliminates the need for using transformers to change from one impedance to another. RG 8/ is a heavy-duty, low-loss coaxial cable with an impedance of 52 ohms. It is about 0.4 inch in diameter and is usually used for the base station antenna. RG 58/U is a thinner cable with the same impedance. It is about 0.2 inch in diameter, but has twice the loss of the heavier cable. It is used in a mobile installation because of its size. Since only a short run of it is needed in a mobile system, the added losses are of no consequence.

QUARTER-WAVE GROUND-PLANE ANTENNA

The evolution of the quarter-wave ground-plane antenna was described above. It is the most commonly used antenna for base station use. It is effective, light in weight, easy to put up, and economical.

Fig. 11-3. Ground-plane antenna
(quarter-wavelength).

Fig. 11-4. Ground-plane antenna
(half-wavelength).

Fig. 11-3 shows a ground-plane antenna, which sells for less than $10.00. It includes a built-in SO-239 connector which takes the PL-259 cable plug; now considered standard for connecting coaxial cable. Cable may be purchased with this plug already installed, simplifying installation. This antenna is used in the detailed installation instructions given in the next chapter for a base station.

HALF-WAVE GROUND-PLANE ANTENNA

The name of this antenna may sound like a misnomer, as any antenna must be a half-wave in length to resonate. But as we have learned, antennas have become named for the vertical element only, which is a quarter-wave long. The other quarter-wave is found in the bent radials or the car body. The half-wave ground-plane antenna is named for the vertical element also. However, with its ground-plane radials and a phasing-transformer stub added into the total length, it is electrically a full-wavelength long. An antenna will not only resonate at a half wavelength, but at multiples of the half-wave in length, also. Thus, an antenna will resonate at or near 27 MHz if it is 17½ feet, 35 feet, 52½ feet, etc.

A half-wave ground-plane antenna is a quarter-wave ground plane with another half-wave length of vertical section added. It is not the full physical length that is added, but a modification to prevent the antenna from becoming too long and unwieldy. The vertical portion is one-half wavelength long, the radials are one-quarter wavelength long, and the other quarter-wavelength is in a stub at the base, acting like a transformer. The Archer "Super Maxim" (Fig. 11-4) is an antenna of this kind.

The Archer "Super Maxim" half-wave CB base-station antenna has been measured to have a gain of 3.75 dB over conventional quarter-wave antennas. This represents an increase of nearly 2½ times in effective radiated power in transmitting and an equivalent increase in sensitivity in receiving. (The dB is mathematically 10 times the log of the number representing the ratio of those two powers.)

COLINEAR ANTENNA

The colinear antenna is an improved method of adding another half-wave in length to an antenna. The two half-wave lengths are "in phase," and result in improved directivity characteristics.

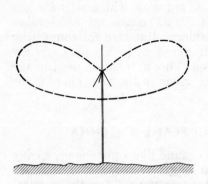

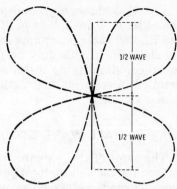

Fig. 11-5. Radiation pattern (side view) of a half-wave antenna mounted vertically.

Fig. 11-6. Overhead view of a full-wave horizontal antenna radiation pattern.

Fig. 11-5 is the radiation pattern (sideview) of a half-wave antenna mounted vertically. This is the pattern developed by the quarter-wave ground-plane antenna, which is really a half-wave antenna when the quarter-wave radials are included. The doughnut-shaped pattern is distorted because of the effect of ground reflection. It develops from the figure 8 pattern of half-wave horizontal antennas.

Two half-wave antennas in line, or a full-wave horizontal antenna, have a double figure 8 pattern or a clover-leaf pattern (Fig. 11-6). A similar vertical antenna would have a pattern like Fig. 11-7, taking into account the reflection of the ground. When two half-wave antennas are connected in line and a stub

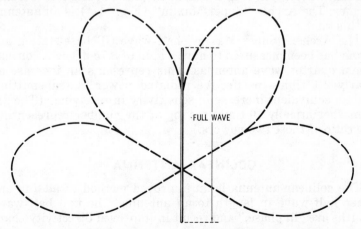

Fig. 11-7. Radiation pattern of a vertical full-wave antenna.

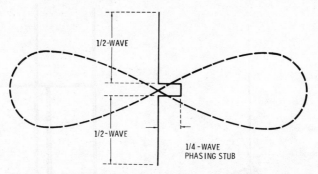

Fig. 11-8. Overhead view of two half-wave horizontal antennas
radiation pattern.

is added between, the two half-wave lengths become in phase,
resulting in an elongated figure 8 pattern (Fig. 11-8). Make
this into a vertical antenna and note the pattern (Fig. 11-9).
Now we have improved low-angle radiation and an increase in
radiated power.

Fig. 11-10 shows the Archer Colinear base-station antenna.
It has a measured effective increase in power over a regular
half-wave type (quarter-wave ground-plane) of 4 dB. With
the antenna five-eights of a wavelength long, we now have an
equivalent to over 2½ times the effective radiated power. To
put it in another way, it is as though your 5-watt transmitter
(the legal maximum power limit) had an input power of
12.55 watts. By making the upper vertical sections five-eights
wavelength long, the radials one-quarter wavelength long, and
the balance in a phasing network at the base, the length of
the vertical element is kept to a very reasonable span of 19 feet,
10 inches.

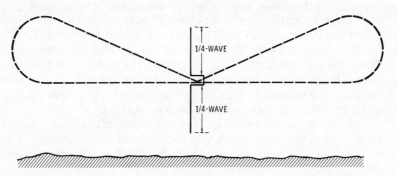

Fig. 11-9. Radiation pattern of a half-wave vertically mounted antenna.

Fig. 11-10. Colinear base-station antenna.

Fig. 11-11. "Crossbow III" beam antenna.

BEAM ANTENNA

Talk to any amateur radio man and he will tell you, when physical dimensions permit, his most effective antenna is a beam antenna. This is a type of construction similar to that described for tv antennas earlier in this book, but with a higher efficieny due to the much narrower bandwidth over which they operate. The increased forward gain and the higher front-to-back ratio results in an effective power gain many times that of a standard half-wave antenna.

The Archer "Crossbow III" CB beam antenna shown in Fig. 11-11 is a three-element array on a 12-foot boom. It has a forward gain of 9 dB, which means that the 5-watt input to a CB transceiver becomes equivalent to 40 watts into an ordinary half-wave antenna. For a serious CB enthusiast this is a considerable increase and well worth the added investment. The front-to-back ratio is 25 dB, which means the antenna has a 25 dB higher sensitivity in pickup from the front than from the rear. This is a great help in reducing the received level of interfering stations which may be in the opposite direction as well as increasing the signal of the desired station.

Unless one is interested in only communicating between two fixed points, the beam must also be mounted atop a rotator, like one of those described in Chapter 9. For full efficiency, wide-area coverage, it is necessary to be able to turn the beam to the direction of communication.

MOBILE ANTENNAS

The greatest feature in operating Citizens band is the ability to communicate between a car and home or office, at a small investment in equipment. Most CB transceivers today use solid-state circuitry, are small, and are easily mounted under the dash of a car. All that is necessary is to mount an antenna and connect it.

Most CB mobile antennas are pretty much alike, differing only in details. The similarity lies in the use of a quarter-wave vertical element, with the car body acting as the other quarter-wave, for a half-wave theoretical antenna. They differ in the method of mounting, in general construction, and in the use of loading coils in some cases to reduce the length of the vertical element.

The first consideration in the selection of a mobile antenna is to decide where it is to be mounted on the car. The best place electrically is on top of the car roof. This results in the best omnidirectional pattern because the mass of the car body is evenly distributed under the antenna. The drawback in roof

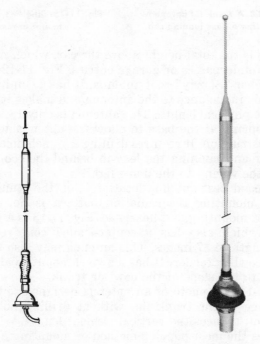

Fig. 11-12. Roof antenna.   Fig. 11-13. Cowl or trunk lid antenna.

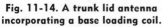

Fig. 11-14. A trunk lid antenna incorporating a base loading coil.

Fig. 11-15. Single-strap bumper-mount antenna.

mounting is the total height above the car, which might inter-fere with underpasses or garage entries. Fig. 11-12 is a sketch of the Archer "Shorty" roof antenna. It has a coil in the center which adds inductance to the antenna and makes it possible to reduce the physical length. This antenna is only 18 inches high. It has a spring at the base to allow the antenna to bend if it hits an obstruction. It requires drilling a ⅜ inch hole in the roof of the car and running the lead-in behind the roof upholster-ing, like the wiring to the dome light.

The second best antenna location is on the trunk lid. With trunk-lid mounting the radiation pattern is not as circular as for roof mounting, but nearly so. Fig. 11-13 is a photo of an antenna which also has a center-loaded coil, reducing the overall length to 37 inches. This antenna may also be mounted onto the cowl or fender. It has a swivel mount to allow for ad-justment to the slope of the cowl or trunk.

Fig. 11-14 is a photo of an antenna designed to be fastened to the edge of the trunk lid, without drilling holes. A base loading coil reduces the vertical element length.

Perhaps the most popular method of mounting a mobile an-tenna is on the bumper. It is the easiest place to mount an an-

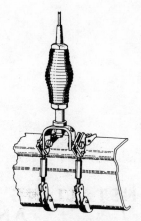

Fig. 11-16. Double-chain system for mounting on a bumper.

tenna, and one which most easily permits its removal without leaving telltale marks. Fig. 11-15 shows the Archer bumper-mount antenna using a single strap for mounting. The vertical element is made of fiberglass with the quarter-wave inside the fiberglass.

The antenna in Fig. 11-16 uses a double chain system of mounting to the bumper. This one and the one shown in Fig. 11-15 have springs at the bottom to allow easy bending when hitting overhead obstructions. This antenna has a 102-inch vertical element.

While bumper mounting is the easiest, it also results in the greatest distortion of the radiation pattern. If it is mounted on the left side of the rear bumper, there is a slight beaming effect towards the right front.

This antenna, and another shorty for mounting to the rain gutter for temporary installations, are the subject of a detailed how-to-install-it story in Chapter 13.

CHAPTER 12

INSTALLING FIXED STATION CB ANTENNAS

Class D Citizens band communication takes place in the 27 MHz band. At this comparatively low frequency, radio waves can be radiated in two ways. One is the sky wave. Radio waves are radiated out at an upward angle and are reflected back by the ionosphere. Sky-wave signals can reach out several thousands of miles (Fig. 12-1). Communication by the sky wave is illegal to CB equipment users.

The other form is the ground wave, which is radiation almost parallel to the plane of the earth's surface. This is like the radiation of tv signals at the higher frequencies described in earlier chapters of this book. The communication path for the ground wave is almost line-of-sight (Fig. 12-2).

Since communication is limited to ground-wave radiation, it becomes necessary to try to accomplish two conditions. That is, use the highest possible gain antenna, and mount it as high as possible. If communication over short distances meets requirements, it is not necessary to use great heights. But the higher the antenna, the farther out is the horizon, and the greater the distance of communication.

Since Citizens band communication is available to every citizen of the United States, without examination, the FCC felt some limits must be placed on communication range to reduce as much as possible interference between stations. This was in anticipation of thousands of stations coming on the air, a forecast that was realized. The limits are to the power of the transmitter (five watts input to the final stage), and the height of the antenna.

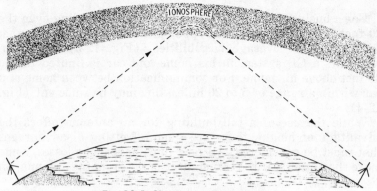

Fig. 12-1. Sky-wave communication.

HEIGHT

Section 95.37 of FCC Regulations on Class D CB says that the antenna and its support must not be more than 20 feet above ground or an existing structure on which it may be mounted; nor can it be above the top of an existing mast now supporting some other communications antenna. The height of an omnidirectional antenna and its support must not exceed 60 feet above ground.

Fig. 12-2. Ground-wave communication.

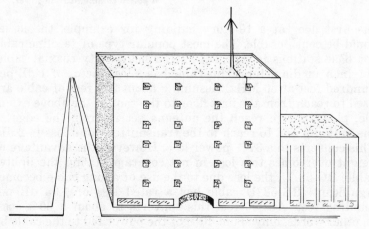

Fig. 12-3. A CB antenna mounted on a building.

For a business with offices in a multi-story building even the 20-foot limit offers excellent opportunities for a high antenna, with excellent coverage possibilities. (Fig. 12-3). The man who puts a CB system in his home and car is limited to the 20 feet above his home. For communication between home and car within a range of 5 to 20 miles, this may be sufficient (Fig. 12-4).

While the use of a tall building for an antenna offers the advantage of height, there are some offsetting disadvantages that must be considered. All feed lines have some losses, some more than others. If the transmitter is far from the antenna, on

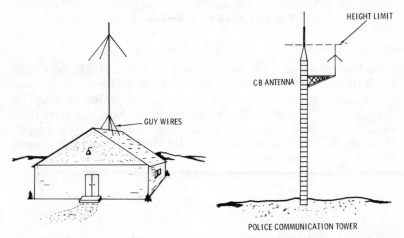

Fig. 12-4. Roof mounted CB antenna.   Fig. 12-5. A CB antenna mounted on a police communication tower.

the first floor of a 10-story building for example, the losses could be considerable. The most popular type of feedline cable for base stations is type RG-8/U, a heavy-duty coaxial cable, 0.4 inch in diameter. This cable has a loss factor of 1 dB per hundred feet at 30 MHz. Assuming about 200 feet of cable are used to reach from the first floor to the roof of the above example, plus some to reach the antenna set in from the edge of the building and to reach to the transmitter, total loss is 2 dB. This converts to a 37% power loss. However, the advantage of height overcomes this loss in net coverage. Using the lighter cable, RG-58/U, the loss due to the use of a long cable becomes significant. RG-58/U cable has a rated loss of 1.95 dB per hundred feet. At 200 feet this converts to about a 60% loss. In other words, only about 40% of the power fed to the cable by the transmitter ever reaches the antenna. Obviously, in this example, investment in the heavier cable, or locating the station in an upper floor of the building, is worthwhile.

As a general rule, the heavier coaxial cable is nearly always used for base station installations. The lighter cable is used for mobile installations.

The "top of an existing mast" mentioned before deserves some clarification, using an example. CB emergency groups are frequently working with local police departments. A CB base-station antenna may be installed on the same tower supporting the police transmitting antenna, thus providing even greater height than the 20-foot limit (Fig. 12-5). Under this condition, the top of the CB antenna must not be above the top of the mast structure. That means the base of the antenna must be mounted about nine feet below the top of the mast on an extension arm.

HOME ROOF MOUNTING

CB base station antennas mount to the same type of mast as tv antennas. The U-bolt mounting clamps are the same. Any of the methods of mounting described in Chapter 7 for tv antenna mounting also apply to CB antennas. The antennas are made of aluminum tubing and are very light. They even have less wind resistance than a tv antenna.

Mast heights may be anywhere from five feet to the 20-foot legal limit. Five- or ten-foot masts are mounted in the same manner as for tv antennas, but 20-foot masts should include guy wires about half-way up (Fig. 12-4). Guying rings are available which slip onto the mast and fasten near the center. The rings contain holes for threading the guy wires through them. Use three guy wires. Forming a triangle, bring the wires down to heavy-duty screw hooks or rings. These should be screwed into the roof at points where they will reach down to the roof rafters, for a secure hold.

The step-by-step installation information that follows is based on installing an Archer ground plane CB base-station antenna. This is an inexpensive antenna but effective in performing as a standard ground plane antenna. It is all-aluminum in construction and includes a built-in jack for accepting the standard PL-259 type plug.

The antenna is supplied in knockdown form, as are all such antennas. It consists of eight aluminum rods, about four feet long and four a little longer. The shorter rods are smaller in diameter and fit into the longer rods. Together they make up the quarter-wavelength for each element. The rods and mounting bracket are predrilled, and all hardware is furnished,

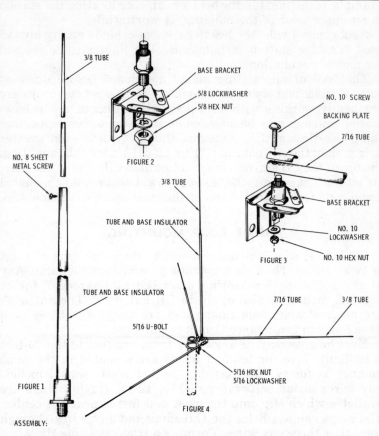

3/8 TUBE

BASE BRACKET

5/8 LOCKWASHER

5/8 HEX NUT

NO. 10 SCREW

BACKING PLATE

7/16 TUBE

NO. 8 SHEET METAL SCREW

FIGURE 2

3/8 TUBE

BASE BRACKET

TUBE AND BASE INSULATOR

NO. 10 LOCKWASHER

NO. 10 HEX NUT

FIGURE 3

TUBE AND BASE INSULATOR

7/16 TUBE

3/8 TUBE

5/16 U-BOLT

5/16 HEX NUT

5/16 LOCKWASHER

FIGURE 1

FIGURE 4

ASSEMBLY:

( ) UNPACK THE ANTENNA AND BECOME FAMILIAR WITH THE PARTS IN THE ILLUSTRATIONS AND IN THE PARTS LIST.

( ) ASSEMBLE THE 7/16 RADIATOR TUBE (WITH BASE INSULATOR) AND 3/8 TUBE AS SHOWN IN FIGURE 1.

( ) ASSEMBLE THE THREE OTHER & 7/16 AND 3/8 RADIAL TUBES IN A SIMILAR MANNER.

( ) ATTACH THE THREE RADIAL TUBING ASSEMBLIES TO THE BRACKET AS IN FIGURE 3.

( ) ASSEMBLE RADIATOR TUBE ASSEMBLY (WITH BASE INSULATOR) INTO BASE BRACKET AS IN FIGURE 2.

INSTALLATION:

( ) INSERT THE U-BOLT IN ITS HOLES, PUT ON THE LOCKWASHERS AND START THE NUTS.

( ) ATTACH THE COAX TO THE ANTENNA USING A PL-259 CONNECTOR AND SEAL THE CONNECTION WITH PLY-O-BOND OR SOME SIMILAR PRODUCT.

( ) PLACE THE ANTENNA ON THE MAST SO THE TOP OF THE MAST IS EVEN WITH THE TOP OF THE BRACKET. (FIGURE 4)

( ) TAPE THE COAX TO THE MAST EVERY FEW FEET.

Fig. 12-6. Antenna assembly instructions.

Fig. 12-7. Closeup of lead-in and antenna mounting.

as well as instructions for assembly. Self-tapping screws are supplied for the two lengths of rods. They have a hex head and are slotted. Either a screwdriver or a ¼-inch hex driver may be used—the latter is easier to use. Only a minimum of simple tools are needed altogether.

The far end of the larger rods are predrilled to take No. 10 machine screws; used to assemble the rods to the base plate. Lock washers are supplied for them and for the threaded U-bolt, which goes around the mast. Backing plates are used over the rods at the base plate under the screw heads. This gives added strength to rod assemblies.

The instructions are very easy to follow (Fig. 12-6). They are given in words and sketches. Once they are read over, and the parts are inspected carefully as the instructions are read, assembly becomes automatic.

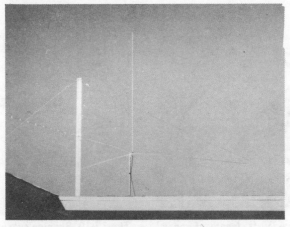

Fig. 12-8. Completed ground-plane antenna.

Assembly may be done on the ground, or on the roof. It is easier on the ground. While the completed antenna is very light, it is a bit cumbersome to take up onto the roof with its nine-foot spider legs going out in all directions. If assembled on the roof, care must be taken to be sure small parts don't roll off.

The U-bolt clamps around the mast. Fig. 12-7 shows this in closeup. Fig. 12-8 shows the completed antenna, ready to be put into operation.

CONNECTING THE FEEDLINE

The feedpoint of a ground-plane antenna is around 50 ohms in impedance. The coaxial cable mentioned in Chapter 11 is the choice for feeding the antenna from the transceiver, and they have an impedance of 52 ohms which is right for the CB antenna. These are RG-8/U heavy-duty cables with an outer diameter of 0.4 inch, and RG-58/U cables with an outer diameter of 0.2 inch. The heavier is preferred for base station use. Coaxial cable may be purchased in any length from bulk stock and in precut lengths in packages. The best way to buy it is in precut lengths with connectors already installed, for home use such as the antenna installation example just described. These are packaged in 50-foot lengths (Fig. 12-9). This cable includes two PL-259 type plugs already installed on the ends. Its length is just about right for the average home installation.

Connect the cable plug to the antenna as shown in the closeup view of Fig. 12-7. Bring it straight down and tape it to the mast at one or two points, depending on the length of the mast.

Fig. 12-9. A 50-ft. length of coaxial cable.

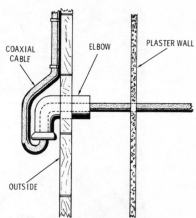

Fig. 12-10. Running coaxial cable through a wall.

Run it into the house about the same as you would tv cable, except that the standoff insulators made for tv cables are too small to take RG-8/U. It does not matter if the cable is near metal, because it has a shield under the outer cover. Any method of securing it to the house or building will do as long as the cable is not punctured in the process.

One of the best methods of bringing this cable into the house is through a hole in the wall opposite the operating position. A plumbing elbow whose inside diameter is at least twice the outside diameter of the cable should be installed with the outside opening facing downward (Fig. 12-10). This makes a waterproof entrance. Once brought through, the inside wall of the hole may be plastered around the cable to keep out the cold winter winds.

If the 50-foot cable is a bit longer than needed, just coil up the remainder under the operating table. There is not enough loss in the use of a small extra amount to warrant cutting it to exact length and installing a plug. There is only a 12% loss in the entire length of 50 feet of RG-8/U cable, so a few extra feet over will represent only a small percentage of the 12%.

The other end of the cable with its plug installed is merely screwed onto the output terminal of the transceiver or whatever CB equipment is used.

The end of this chapter shows how to connect PL-259 plugs to cables cut to length.

GROUNDING FOR PROTECTION

Unlike a tv antenna, a CB antenna has a vertical element that reaches up fairly high into the sky. This vertical element is insulated from the mounting plate and the mast. It connects to the center conductor of the cable feeding the antenna. This means that grounding the mast, as in tv installations, is not enough for a CB antenna. Instead, the center-insulated element must be protected from lightning.

Fig. 12-11 shows a lightning arrester made for coaxial cable. There is a small spark gap between the outer shell and the inner conductor. Since CB power is low, the gap can be narrow without the transmitter power jumping it, but any static charge on the antenna will.

This coaxial lightning-arrester has a PL-259 plug at one end and a SO-239 socket at the other. It connects between the cable and the antenna, at the antenna. A heavy ground wire, usually aluminum, is connected to the screw on the side of the shell and

Fig. 12-11. Coaxial lightning arrester.

run to a ground rod in the earth, the same as for tv antenna protection.

When the CB antenna is completely installed, it is well to give all connectors a coating of Ply-O-Bond and smear all hardware with some silastic rubber or silicone seal. These will seal those parts against the effects of the atmosphere, and lengthen the life of the antenna.

INSTALLING COAXIAL CABLE CONNECTORS

When bulk coaxial cable is used, the ends must be dressed, and PL-259 plugs installed onto the ends. This takes some dexterity and some experience in soldering, although there are some solderless types of plugs.

The sketch of Fig. 12-12 shows how the ends of the cable are dressed. The inner conductor is soldered to the center pin of

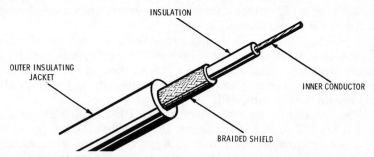

INSULATION

OUTER INSULATING JACKET

INNER CONDUCTOR

BRAIDED SHIELD

Fig. 12-12. Coaxial cable prepared for soldering to connector.

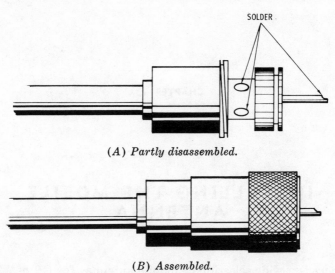

SOLDER

(A) *Partly disassembled.*

(B) *Assembled.*

Fig. 12-13. Coaxial cable connector.

the plug. Since the pin protrudes out slightly in front of the shell, the inner conductor of the cable is made slightly longer than the rest of the cable parts. The braided outer conductor is soldered to the shell of the plug. The length of each cut on the cable is easily determined by laying it against the plug.

Remove the outer screw from the plug, and slide the plug onto the cable, well below the end. Insert the cable into the plug, and solder the center conductor to the pin of the plug. Solder the braided shield to the neck of the outer shell through two of the holes in the neck. This is more easily done by pre-tinning the shielded braid before inserting the cable. It will take a hot soldering iron to solder through the holes of the plug. This is shown in Fig. 12-13A. Sketch B of this figure shows the completed assembly, after the outer screw-on shell is slid up and screwed back into place.

CHAPTER 13

INSTALLING THE MOBILE ANTENNA

There is a wide selection of mobile antennas for CB use. The basic kinds were described in Chapter 11. Each one comes with complete instructions on how to mount them on a car. Considering that one is working at ground level, it is not difficult to install a mobile CB antenna. However, those that mount on a metal surface pose a problem in the need to cut a large hole in the car's fender or roof. These can be cut by using an electric drill to make a small starting hole, then using a hand brace with a tapered reamer for enlarging.

There are alternatives to drilling into the car body. The two mobile antennas, whose installation is described in the following paragraphs, require no drilling, and are easily removable for use on another car.

GUTTER-MOUNT ANTENNA

The simplest antenna mount is to use the rain gutter at the side roof line of the car. The antenna merely clamps to the rolled-up edge of the rain gutter. The accompanying illustrations cover the installation of the Radio Shack gutter-mount antenna. It is only 18 inches high, but has a loading coil that makes it an electrical ¼ wave long. It has attached to it a length of RG-58/U cable which has a PL-259 plug attached on the end. It comes ready to be immediately plugged into the CB transceiver in the car.

Because of its small size and ease of installation and removal, the gutter-mount antenna is intended for temporary use. Although its short length reduces the risk of hitting low over-

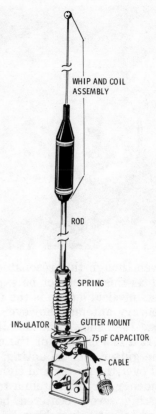

WHIP AND COIL
ASSEMBLY

ROD

SPRING

INSULATOR   GUTTER MOUNT

75 pF CAPACITOR

CABLE

**Fig. 13-1. Gutter-mount antenna
construction.**

passes and other solid obstructions, a spring at the bottom will
give when obstructions, such as low overhanging tree branches,
are hit, with no damage to the antenna.

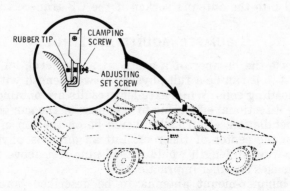

RUBBER TIP   CLAMPING
SCREW

ADJUSTING
SET SCREW

Fig. 13-2. Gutter clamp.

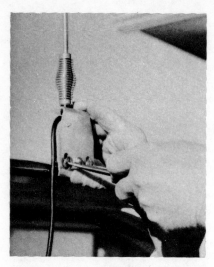

Fig. 13-3. Mounting the antenna.

Even though this resonates in the CB band, an antenna as short as this must not be expected to give the results of one whose physical length is the full ¼ wave for resonating. For a temporary antenna, however, results are good.

Fig. 13-1 shows the details of the gutter-mount antenna. Fig. 13-2 is a closeup of the clamp which holds to the inside of the gutter. For mounting, the clamp is first loosened, then fitted over the gutter and tightened. When held firmly, there is a tendency for the antenna to bend towards the car body. An adjusting screw centered between the clamping screws is turned in until its rubber tip presses against the car body to push the antenna into an upright position.

Fig. 13-3 shows the antenna being mounted to the gutter of a car. The cable is fed in through the window, and the plug screwed into the antenna socket of the CB transceiver.

BUMPER-MOUNT ANTENNA

Because the bumper of a car is at a low level, an antenna mounted to it can be a full physical ¼-wavelength without the use of loading coils. While excellent results are obtained, there is some directional effect due to the mass of the car body. The ideal installation, electrically, would be on the top of the car body, in the center of the roof. But an antenna physically a quarter-wave in length would extend nine feet above the roof, which makes it rather impractical.

The bumper-mount antenna to be described here uses a double-chain mounting system, which is more rigid than a

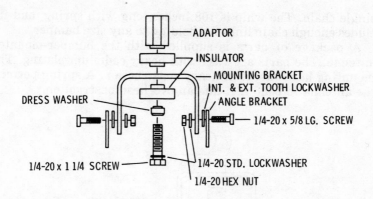

Fig. 13-4. Assembly of mounting bracket.

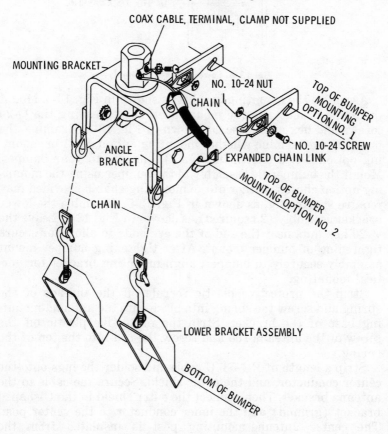

Fig. 13-5. Bumper mount details.

single chain. The whip is 108 inches long with spring, and includes enough chain links for holding to any size bumper.

A package of parts is supplied with the bumper-mounted antenna. The parts are steel with heavy cadmium plating. The mounting hardware is of heavy construction. A spring permits the antenna to bend if it hits an overhead obstruction.

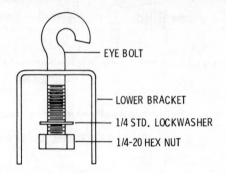

Fig. 13-6. Lower bracket assembly.

Assemble the mounting bracket as shown in Fig. 13-4. Mount the angle brackets to the mounting bracket, leaving the ¼-20 screws and hex nuts loose, as shown in Fig. 13-4. Examine the bumper to determine whether mounting option No. 1 or mounting option No. 2 shown in Fig. 13-5 adapts to your bumper. Mount the bumper tie assembly to the bumper using the mounting option chosen. Either of the mounting chains provided may require shortening, as shown in Fig. 13-5. Assemble the lower bracket assembly (2 required) as shown in Fig. 13-6. Leave the ¼-20 hex nuts near the end of the eye bolts to allow for secure tightening of bumper mount. After tightening bumper mount assembly securely to bumper, align mounting bracket for vertical mounting.

Strip the protective plastic ferrule off the threads of the spring and screw the spring into place onto the antenna-mounting base of the bracket. Strip the protective plastic off the screw of the antenna rod and screw the rod into the top of the spring.

Strip a length of RG-58/U cable and solder the lugs onto the center conductor, and the outer shield. Secure the cable to the antenna bracket. Then connect the outer shield to the U-shaped bracket (ground) and the inner conductor to the center post. The center antenna mounting post is insulated from the bracket.

Recheck your work to make sure it is secure and that no part of the vertical section of the antenna, including the spring and base of the bracket, touches any part of the car. It is better to adjust the bracket slightly off the vertical than risk the antenna parts touching the car and shorting out.

The feeder cable can be run to the transceiver in either of two methods. One is to run it under the car chassis, into the motor compartment, and back through the firewall to the transceiver. A good grade of plastic tape should be used to fasten the cable to nonmoving parts of the chassis underneath. The other method is to go into the trunk, through the wall between the trunk and the back seat, and under the edge of the carpet to the transceiver. This is the method used most, and is rather easy to do. The cable is less than ¼-inch thick and easily fits along the edge under the carpeting.

CHECKING MOBILE ANTENNA PERFORMANCE

If you have read through the tv sections of this book, you will remember references to impedance matching and standing waves on the feeder. Impedance matching between the antenna and the transceiver is important in CB equipment as well, and especially for mobile installations, because of the low height and the need to get every milliwatt of energy into the air.

The output of a transceiver in its transmit position is designed for a 50-ohm load. The characteristic impedance of RG-58/U cable is 50 to 52 ohms. If the antenna connected to the cable is resonant, its load impedance is very nearly 50 ohms. Therefore, a resonant antenna is the proper load for the transceiver, and no adjustments are necessary.

An antenna which is resonant at a frequency other than the operating frequency will not "look" like a proper load to the transceiver, and there will be a loss of output power due to the mismatch. An antenna can be made to resonate at the operating frequency by the simple means of changing its length. But you must first know whether the antenna is or is not resonant, and if not, whether you are nearing resonance as you adjust its length. This is done by making measurements with an inexpensive instrument called a CB tester.

The photo of Fig. 13-6 shows the Realistic CB Tester. It requires no external power to operate it. It works from the power output of the transceiver. It is one of several standing-wave ratio (swr) instruments; the more expensive ones measure the swr of high-powered transmitters. Adjusting for minimum swr, adjusts for resonance and impedance match between transmitter and antenna. The Realistic unit does more than measure swr. It also measures percent of modulation. It may be connected at the transceiver and left in the feeder line permanently for observation of antenna performance and modulation.

Connect the CB tester between the feeder line and the antenna. Turn the transceiver on and lock it in transmit position. Have the channel selector on a channel near the center of the CB band. Set the center knob of the CB tester on "swr cal" and adjust the right-hand knob for full scale setting of the meter needle. Turn the center knob to swr and read the meter. If it reads between 1:1 and 1:1.2 you are close enough to resonance for excellent performance and no adjustment need be made to the antenna. If the swr reading is higher than 1:2 some antenna length adjustment is necessary.

Fig. 13-7. CB tester.

The gutter-mount antenna described above is easy to adjust. Loosen the knurled lock nut at the bottom of the coil and slide the coil up or down on the lower section of the vertical portion of the rod. With each adjustment of length, make a new measurement of swr. Each time the swr is measured the instrument must be recalibrated.

The bumper-mounted antenna is a full 108 inches long with the spring in place (the spring adds 6 inches to the length). At its full length, it is nearly resonant to 26 MHz. To test this antenna, set up the swr bridge (CB tester) as for the gutter-mounted antenna. The swr will probably be above

1:2. Using heavy-duty wire cutters, or a hack saw, cut one-half inch off the top and make a new measurement. If still not close enough, repeat the cutting operation and remeasure. It may take as many as 10 of these cuts to reach resonance, but it is advisable to take it a little at a time to prevent going past the point of best swr.

INDEX